The Konar
and the Apple

Fun, Beauty, and Dread—From Ahwaz to California

Babak Hodjat

Praise for Babak Hodjat's *The Konar and the Apple*

"At once charming and chilling, *The Konar and the Apple* leaps from memories of invented childhood games and hijinks to traumatic images of the domestic disruption of revolution, war with Iraq, and the growing pains of the new Islamic Republic. A master storyteller, Hodjat invites the reader to take a front-row seat, witnessing a life lived with love and intention, yet always open to startling new adventures."

- Elizabeth Papp Kamali, Deputy Dean, Harvard Law School

"We sit next to Babak Hodjat, and we live his moments through his eyes, words and emotions. In his deadpan humor, disarming simplicity, and authenticity, he shows us how extraordinary circumstances and ordinary, everyday decisions shape one's life. A beautiful kaleidoscope of a journey."

- Antoine Blondeau, Founder, AIQ

"As someone who grew up in the Middle East and was also uprooted by war, I found Babak's stories relatable and endearing. Babak's writing and his attention to the little details brought his childhood to life, transporting me to Iran, in the middle of the Kooy, Ahwaz's university housing campus where he grew up."

- Dr. Rana el Kaliouby, New York Times bestselling author of *Girl Decoded*

"We rarely learn the back stories of today's technology leaders – but here Babak Hodjat eloquently, entertainingly and compellingly recounts a coming-of-age journey through war, revolution... and love."

- David Rowan, Founding Editor-in-Chief, *WIRED UK* and author of *Non-Bullshit Innovation*

"It's amazing that one of the foremost AI minds on the planet would also be gifted with the ability to tell simple, human stories so beautifully. A charming and captivating book."
- Stuart D'Rozario, CEO & Chief Creative Officer, DRZP, D'Rozario & Partners

"An incredible story of an Iranian boy who ended up being a successful entrepreneur in Silicon Valley, the mecca of innovative start-ups. Even more amazing is that Babak moved to Silicon Valley via Japan as a springboard. The cross pollination of the three cultures of Iran, Japan and the U.S. provides readers with a powerful message about the meaning of life."
- Hiroshi Menjo, Managing Partner at NSV Wolf Capital and bestselling author of *Secret of Silicon Valley*

"What makes these coming-of-age stories of innocence and wonder so compelling is that they are told against the backdrop of growing up in the Islamist Republic of Iran. Hovering just behind the gentle banter of teenage boys at play are the regime's tentacles reaching everywhere, even to the narrator's hair, but also tearing a tight-knit family asunder."
- Micha X. Peled, Award-winning independent filmmaker, *The Globalization Trilogy: STORE WARS, China Blue, Bitter Seeds*

TABLE OF CONTENTS

STORIES

*I*t's all about the story. People like stories. They remember them easily, and it gives them something to talk about. Stories are much more significant to us than we realize. Most of us make the more important decisions of our lives simply because it makes 'our stories' more interesting, and all else is detail.

These are my stories.

I started writing them down to pass time during my train commute. I read the one about the soccer board game for my brother, Siamak, and my friends, Kaivan and Masoud. There was some dispute about the game scores, and Siamak made fun of the way I had described the Italy-Algeria incident, but, overall, I think they liked it.

When I told Mom I was writing the story of the board game, I was surprised by her reaction.

We were video chatting and the picture, coming from Tehran, was grainy, but I still picked up on her concerned expression.

"You must understand, Babak, it was a special circumstance. I had to do what I did, or you would not have succeeded."

For the first time I realized that, all this time, she had been carrying some sort of guilt about the whole affair. I hope I've done justice to her in the stories. I love her.

My wife, Jila, has encouraged me and keeps asking me to read her the stories. I don't know if she'd like them. She has some great stories of her own, and my stories pale in comparison to hers. I'm afraid I'd bore her. She's heard them all from me anyway, and all I've done here is simply write them down.

I've yet to read any for my kids. They are too busy making their own stories. Maybe they'll read them later, when they are older, and perhaps the stories will inspire them to write down theirs.

But I won't dedicate this to anyone.

These are my stories.

COAGULATION

*F*unny how you keep revisiting some embarrassing childhood stories. When I was eight or nine, our teacher asked a question of the class that I thought had an obvious answer, and I raised my hand.

"Excuse me, Ma'am," I said, hoping she would pick me to answer.

I didn't usually volunteer to answer questions. I wasn't that good a student and I preferred anonymously slipping under the radar, evading all attention as much as possible. But the answer seemed obvious to me.

"Babak," she said, nodding at me, and I stood up, smiling proudly.

"My dad is a biologist, and so I know the answer," I said. "When there is an injury and blood is coming out of a wound, it has a chemical reaction with the outside of the vein, and that makes blood become solid."

"Your father told you that?" the teacher asked.

"Yes!" I lied, proudly.

The teacher looked at the other students. "Does anyone else want to answer?"

Why would anyone else want to answer? I thought.

One of the girls raised her hand.

"Go ahead Negar," the teacher said.

"When there's an injury, blood packets are sliced open by the tear in

3

the skin, which triggers the clotting," said Negar.

I started to laugh. *What the heck is she talking about? Did she just make that up?*

The teacher nodded. "That is correct, Negar. Well done."

I couldn't believe my ears. How could she be right? *That just totally doesn't make any sense whatsoever.*

"But... my dad said..." I protested.

A few of the kids chuckled and the teacher gave me a funny smile.

"You can sit down now, Babak."

As I sat down, completely embarrassed, my brain was rushing to find an explanation for what had just happened. Why was I so sure of the answer? Why did I have to lie about my dad? Why was the process of blood-clotting so strange and complex?

***

Thirty-some years later, I was taking a walk with a doctor friend of mine, and I mentioned the story.

"So yeah," I concluded, "I guess that's one reason I didn't become a doctor. Math is much more obvious and straightforward."

"You wanna know something?" my friend asked.

"What?"

"You were right all along."

"You mean...?"

"About the process of blood clotting," he said. "As soon as a vessel tears, exposure of blood to protein like tissue factor initiates changes to blood platelets and the plasma protein. That starts the coagulation chain reaction."

"Really?" I stood there stunned. "I was right?"

"Yep." He smiled.

"I knew it! How crazy is that? I've been holding this trauma in my head for all these years and I was actually right all along, and she was wrong!" It was almost as if I had taken my revenge. "Wow!"

"Yeah," he said. "In fact, that girl's explanation is so convoluted and wrong, it's laughable."

"Exactly!" I was beyond myself. "That idiot teacher! How she embarrassed me in front of the entire class. And I was right all along."

***

I've been telling this story a lot since then. A story of ultimate vindication. A story with a happy ending that had finally put my mind at ease; that I had not been a crazy young kid. I mean yes, I had lied, a little fib to strengthen my claim, but that can be excused for a child of eight. What can't be excused is the way the teacher had treated me.

***

The other day, I was reading an article about ventilators and how lungs work, and it reminded me of my blood-clotting story and the fact that something had bothered me about it.

Why had the teacher accepted Negar's cockamamie story over mine? Had the teacher not known the answer? Was she so cruel as to go with any other explanation just to embarrass me? Had she sensed that I was lying about my dad? Maybe that had rubbed her the wrong way somehow? But no, I don't remember her as being that kind of a person.

Or maybe this had been the explanation at the time, thirty years ago? Or maybe our schoolbooks had not been updated. No, that can't be either. This had been the mid-seventies, and they would have known something like that by then.

No. I think there's a different explanation. I think, most probably, that my 'obvious' answer had been what I remember Negar as saying. In other words, through the years, my brain had swapped the two explanations. I had remembered my answer to have been the obvious one, but Negar's had been clearly more obvious than mine, and so I had corrected the memory and made her answer mine.

I feel like I spent thirty years believing I had been stupid in that classroom fiasco, then, for ten years, believing I had been vindicated and actually quite smart, and now, I feel I'm back to square one. On top of that, I'm not sure I can trust any of my childhood memories anymore.

How embarrassing.

SHAH'S VISIT

*T*he Shah was coming to town and it was a big deal. The Kooy was abuzz with excitement. Everyone was talking about it, and everyone was preparing as if the Shah were going to pay them a personal visit. Referred to as 'The Shah' in informal circles, all the children at my school were told to refer to him as His Royal Excellency.

Our school library was a separate world from my fifth-grade classroom with Mr. Saadegh, run by his booming voice and engaging style. Library hour was usually quite uneventful. We'd all be very quiet, lying around on the *poshti* cushions on the carpet while we read books or just fell asleep. Other than the occasional hushing, Mrs. Ehsani—our library teacher— would seldom speak to us at all during the whole hour, and we were free to read whichever book we chose. As soon as we entered the library that day, though, we could tell all was different: Mrs. Ehsani had an air of importance about herself.

"OK, kids, you know that His Royal Excellency will be paying a visit to Ahwaz next week."

Ahwaz is a city in Iran's Khuzestan province, where most of Iran's oil comes from, and all of its natural gas. The *Kooyeh Ostadaneh Daaneshgah,* which means Neighborhood of Professors of University, and which everyone just called "the Kooy," was my neighborhood in Ahwaz.

"But did you know," Mrs. Ehsani continued, "that he will also be gracing our school with His presence?"

A bunch of oohs and ahhs went up from the kids.

"The Shah is coming to our school?!" one boy exclaimed.

"His Royal Excellency," Mrs. Ehsani corrected him, "will be visiting our school here, yes." She smiled proudly.

"Oh my God!" Naazila Nayebi added, wide-eyed. "What are we supposed to do? How do we get ready?"

Naazila lived in the Kooy. She was red-haired and freckled, as was her older brother, Naader. Yes, Naader and Naazila. I didn't know either of them well. He was two years older than me, and she was a girl, so we didn't play much.

"This is exactly why I wanted to talk to you, my dears," said Mrs. Ehsani, suddenly softly. "We need to prepare for His Excellency's visit. Everything should be tidied up and cleaned. We should all be well behaved. We should have our uniforms washed and pressed the night before! Your teacher will tell you all about that part. But the library also needs to be presentable."

Everyone was listening. It was exciting to see the Shah in person, but—maybe just in my own mind— there was something wrong with all of it.

"We will divide into five groups. One group will tidy up all the books and make sure they are in proper order. I need a group to check all the index cards and replace the missing ones. The other three groups will make a poster each, which we will hang on the wall: one of a science book, one of a novel, and one for a book of poetry... Yes, Babak?"

"Excuse me, Ma'am," I said, "but why are we doing all this again?"

"Why, weren't you listening, Babak-*jaan*? His Roy—"

"Yes, I understood that part, but isn't he coming to see the school as it is?"

"Well, sure, but..."

"So why should we be doing all of this for him? Isn't that lying?" I didn't usually raise my hand in class. The last time I'd done so, I'd been embarrassed in front of the whole class. But this felt obviously wrong to me, and I simply had to point it out. Of course, Mrs. Ehsani was a very kind and considerate teacher, and I felt safe with her.

"But His..." Mrs. Ehsani started again.

"Yeah," one of the other boys joined in, "we shouldn't lie to the Shah, should we?"

"Dears, His Royal..."

"I don't mind doing all that stuff," said a boy named Vahid. "But we should do it after his visit."

"We shouldn't hide the reality," some girl said.

"He'd see right through it anyway!" proclaimed another girl.

"But..." Mrs. Ehsani was stammering, and the kids were talking over her.

"Yeah, let him see our school as it is," I said, raising my voice just to be part of it all.

"His Excellency must know the truth!"

"He's going to be looking through the index cards?"

"Enough! Enough!" Mrs. Ehsani screamed in her normal voice again, but very high-pitched.

We stopped. We'd never seen her so angry before.

"Enough already!" Her face was red. "Show some respect! It is His Royal Excellency, the *Shahanshah Ariamehr*, you are referring to." She looked at the picture framed on the wall. It was the same picture of Him you could see hung everywhere in the school and on the first page of our schoolbooks.

"He's the father of our nation," she continued, "and I will not have his name be uttered disrespectfully in my library."

She turned to me. "Babak." Then she turned to Vahid. "And Vahid..."

"Yes, Ma'am," we both answered.

She opened the door, pointing out with an open hand, "You will go to the principal's office now."

We stepped out, both looking back at her, both confused.

"But—"

"NOW!" She slammed the door right behind us.

I had been sent to the principal's office before, but this time I had a sense that my crime was more serious. Vahid looked pretty scared too. I didn't know him that well, but felt some degree of responsibility for him. He had followed my lead in the protest.

"We didn't do anything," I whispered to Vahid as we walked, trying to reassure him.

"Why did she call *me* out?" he whispered back. "You started the whole thing."

He did have a point. He was tall and had a deeper voice than most of us, so of course the teachers picked on him more often than he deserved.

"What are you boys doing here?" Principal Rahimi asked when she saw us lingering at her door. Mrs. Rahimi was a beautiful long-haired woman of thirty who had been our second grade teacher and was still the object of a perpetual crush of mine and of half the boys in school.

"Mrs. Ehsani sent us, Ma'am," I said.

"Have you been misbehaving?" she asked, with a fake frown that was given away by a smile that somehow hid beneath.

"I don't think so," I replied.

"Why did Mrs. Ehsani send you here then?"

Something told me to delay telling the truth as long as possible, though maybe back then I just didn't have many strategies to choose from.

"We don't know, Ma'am."

"You don't know?" Vahid looked at me confused, then back at the principal. We both shrugged, innocently.

Mrs. Ehsani sighed. "Very well then, let's ask her."

"We asked her a question, Ma'am," I explained, just as she reached for the intercom. "But everyone was asking questions."

"Mrs. Ehsani?" she said into the device.

There was a lot of noise from the other end. It sounded like the kids had taken over the library.

"Mrs. Ehsani?" she said again, tilting her ear toward the device. "Mrs. Ehsani!"

"See? She can't control her class. We just asked some questions," I said boldly.

Mrs. Rahimi gave up on the intercom and looked at us. She was about to declare some sort of verdict, as she inhaled and opened her mouth.

"Everybody's excited with the news of His Excellency's visit," Vahid blurted out, in a stroke of genius.

A smile broke out on Mrs. Rahimi's face, and the frown on top vanished.

"Isn't it such exciting news?" It was an announcement more than a question.

We both nodded.

"Mrs. Ramazani, did you order those flowers yet?" she shouted over us to one of the assistants. "Please make sure they are delivered by Monday morning so we can set them up. Did you count the carpets?"

She turned to us and said, "Oh my God, do we have enough carpets?"

Then she stood, recovering her principal voice. "We need to prepare the school. This is too important... He is the father of our nation." Then she opened the door just like Mrs. Ehsani did. "Run along to your class and help with the preparation."

We ran out.

"Be good now!" she called after us.

***

When I told Mom about the whole affair that night, she took it very seriously. She made me sit so she could look at me sternly. "Babak, you have to be very careful about these things. You are old enough to use your judgment on such matters."

I wasn't quite sure what she meant, but I nodded. Her tone called for a slow nod.

"There are certain things we might talk about at home that you should not mention at school, do you understand?"

She must have been talking about my dad's affair with the Savak, the Shah's dreaded secret police. Mom and Dad had been at a friends' place and made the mistake of discussing politics there.

"Remember what happened just a few months ago?" Mom asked, confirming my guess. "We criticized the government... in a private visit... with friends of ours, and your dad received a Savak summons the very next week."

"But I didn't criticize the government," I said.

Mom shook her head. "It doesn't matter what you think you did. They'll tell you what you did. There are too many spies around here and we have to be careful."

I still did not know how to follow her advice, but I knew my parents had been made afraid by the Savak incident. Dad said that they were watching him, and that they knew that he asked his students "political questions." My dad was really not political at all, never has been. In one occasion he had asked his class, "How are things these days?" That was the question some student reported.

"OK," I said. "I'll be more careful. By the way, Mrs. Rahimi asked if we had any carpets we could lend to her."

Suddenly my mom smirked. "Carpets, huh?" she said wryly, and didn't even answer.

***

Mr. Saadegh was our idol. He had complete command over us kids, and we devoured every word he spoke. We even repeated some of them to each other during recess. He was funny, always full of stories, and he made us feel like he was on our side. But he had his serious side too, and with his large build and very big head, people took notice when he talked.

"You will all get the best grades from me," he had declared on the first day of school.

He had told us, secretly, that he would give us all A's for our oral exams, and that he would tell us all the answers to the written exams. This was to be our class secret, not to be told to anyone. He had beautiful handwriting, and he could write equally well with his left and right hand. Sometimes, he would write a sentence from both sides, with both hands simultaneously, meeting in the middle and mesmerizing the whole class.

In the days leading up to the Shah's visit, Mr. Saadegh worked harder than ever, helping with the decorations, writing quotes of the Shah on large glossy paper that we hung all around the school, and making us memorize the words to a song praising His Royal Excellency, which we sang at an assembly in front of the principal that Saturday morning.

"My fellow Iranians, marching along, man and woman, on our way to revolution…"

We were singing about the White Revolution. The full name of it was "The White Revolution of the Shah and of the Nation." After we were done singing, Mr. Saadegh took the microphone and talked about the pillars of the Shah's revolution. I knew it was cool to see our homeroom teacher talk to the whole school like that. We were the oldest kids in school, and he was the coolest teacher. The speech, however, went on and on… and on. I don't think anyone was listening, and I don't think the speech was for us in the first place. The ending was good, though:

"Please join me in praising the father of our nation with three loud long-live-the-Shah's…"

"JAVID SHAH! JAVID SHAH! JAVID SHAH!" we all shouted at the top of our lungs.

"Now, kids, with Mrs. Rahimi's permission, I declare the first period as recess," said Mr. Saadegh, and we all exploded into a big cheer.

***

That evening they let us go early while they finished beautifying the school, which was like a beehive of activity when we left. Homework was as light as the schoolday had been. I was done in a few minutes.

"Mom, I'm done with my homework, can I go play with Masoud?"

"You're done already?"

"Yeah!"

"You sure don't seem to have much homework this year."

"Mr. Saadegh doesn't believe in homework."

She paused. "I would have expected more for a fifth grader."

She stopped asking questions, so I decided she was fine with me heading out and I left for Masoud's, which was only a couple minutes' walk from us.

Masoud's mom opened the door, "Hello Babak-jaan."

"Hello, Mrs. Kaameli. Can Masoud come out to play?"

"Oh, he's doing his—"

"I'm done!" Masoud's voice came from the other room.

"Already? You never have more than five minutes!" she exclaimed. Had she been talking to my mom?

"Mr. Saadegh doesn't believe in homework," I told her.

"That's weird," Mrs. Kaameli said. "I'm a teacher too, and the education department recommends a lot of homework for your grade. You know you have nationwide exams this year, don't you?"

I nodded. Everyone had been warning us about that since fourth grade. Everyone but Mr. Saadegh, who had declared on the first day of school that, with him as our teacher, we need not worry about any exams. We were really lucky to have him. He had won Ahwaz's Best Teacher Award three years in a row.

There was never a boring moment with Masoud. We had so many things to do. We played some G.I. Joes in his backyard. He had a full Six-Million-Dollar Man set, complete with a rocket ship to take him to the moon. We then checked on the tadpoles in the fountain. Not too many out yet, but we did spot a few. We climbed the walls enclosing the grass field by his house and sat on top, talking for a while. Then we wondered why no one was out yet, and decided it would be a great idea to get the gang together to play some kickball!

We were going towards the main street to check if Keyhan could play, when the trucks rolled in. Everything happened very quickly. A bunch of workers got off the trucks and started setting down brand new lamp posts along the street. We already had big fluorescent streetlamps but these ones were shorter and much nicer-looking. Other workers were painting yellow lines on the street near the curbs. At the intersection, they were installing a stop sign and a bright yellow postbox—the first for the Kooy.

"Wow!" I said. "All this because the Shah is coming?"

"My dad says yesterday they planted tall palm trees on both sides of the boulevard that goes to the airport," said Masoud.

"If he keeps coming here our town will look like Paris!"

"I guess that'd be OK. Whatever the excuse."

"Yeah, and then a big vacation for all city workers after he's gone," I said sarcastically.

Arash appeared on his tiny little bike, pedaling frantically towards us. "Hey! Guys, bring your bows and arrows!" he said, out of breath. "And your bikes! We're playing Cowboys and Indians in the jungle!"

I looked at Masoud, and we both ran home to get our stuff.

***

I limped home with bruises all over my body that night. Cowboys and Indians was the most fun game we played in the Kooy, but it was pretty dangerous. The Indians hid in trees along the dirt path in a place we called "The Jungle," and they shot arrows at the cowboys racing through on their bikes. They used real bows and shot twigs as arrows, which mostly missed. If they hit you, your bike was theirs, and you became an Indian. Some aimed for the wheels, and every once in a while, the arrow would get stuck in the spokes and stop the bike, throwing the cowboy off his horse. After a few casualties, we outlawed aiming for the front wheel, but mistakes still happened, sometimes intentionally.

I had dirt all over my clothes and in my hair, so I snuck in and headed straight for the bathroom, trying to avoid my parents, who were talking in the living room.

"Look!" Mom was saying to Dad as she handed him a magazine. "He looks just like Mossadegh." She had it open on the "funnies" page.

He looked at it for a moment. "So he does. I wonder if it was intentional."

After taking a shower and slipping into my pajamas, I came looking for the Zan-e-Rooz magazine. There was no newspaper delivery in the Kooy, and my dad would buy the odd magazine or a newspaper from two days ago when he went shopping in the city. I particularly liked Zan-e-Rooz, "Today's Woman," because of its "funnies" pages. I looked at all the cartoons but didn't find anything standing out.

"Which cartoon were you talking about?" I asked, holding up the open magazine to my mom.

"What?"

"When I came in, you and Dad were talking about some guy's cartoon, weren't you?"

Was that a hint of concern in Mom's face?

"Oh, that?" She shook her head. "That was nothing."

It must have been something then.

"Which one was it?" I persisted.

Dad came to Mom's rescue. He took the magazine and pointed at a bald man with a big nose in one of the cartoons. "That's the one. That looks like Mossadegh." He looked at it some more. "But it's probably just a coincidence."

"Who's Mossadegh?" I asked later, as we sat at the dinner table.

Mom looked at Dad, as if to ask him something silently, and Dad nodded back. I really didn't know what was going on and was getting uncomfortable with all the secrecy.

"You don't have to tell me if it's a grown-up thing!" I blurted.

Mom turned her chair to face her whole body toward me.

"Babak, Dr. Mossadegh was Iran's prime minister. He did some very good things for the country, like take back control of the oil. He was beloved by many people, but he got into trouble with the Shah and he was deposed. That's why we don't talk about him in public. Do you understand?"

"Is he dead?"

"Yes, he died years ago," Dad said.

"But you shouldn't mention his name to anyone," Mom insisted. "Even Masoud."

I nodded.

"This is serious, Babak. It can cost your father his job. You don't want that now, do you?"

"OK," I said, feeling important. My parents had let me in on a secret and I was to protect it.

"Good boy."

I thought I'd reciprocate. "By the way, Mrs. Rahimi gave me and Masoud and a couple of our friends a secret mission for tomorrow."

"What?" Mom asked.

"After the Shah passes us, we are to run all the way around the outside of the school and take the carpets he's already walked on to the other side before he gets there."

"What?"

"I told you they're short on carpets, remember?"

"Like a bunch of clowns." Mom rolled her eyes. Dad tried to hide his laugh with his food.

***

No classes Wednesday. Everyone was scurrying around preparing. We all had our best clothes and shoes on and some of the girls looked like little movie stars, with lots of makeup and jewelry and their hair done. Naazila even had a great big rose sticking out of her hair, and a few of the kids made fun of her.

"Did you put it there or did it just grow by itself, Naazila?"

There were flowers everywhere, and the teachers brought baskets of petals for us to toss at the Shah and his contingent as he walked by. There was a news truck parked by the curb next to the schoolyard and some really fancy filming equipment was being offloaded and set up: in front of the school, inside the main entrance, in the cafeteria, and in the hall. Mr. Saadegh, our fifth-grade teacher we all idolized, was wearing a white tuxedo today. He gave another feverish speech, and they made us stand in line in the hallway, along the path the Shah was to take.

Our class ended up somewhere near the end of the hallway, close to an exit. I was a bit worried that we wouldn't have enough time to run all the way around to move the carpets. The students were told not to step on them, so we were leaning against the walls on both sides. All the classroom doors were shut and we couldn't see what was going on outside.

Then someone yelled, "He's here!"

This would happen several times and turn out to not be true. I guess it was probably an honest mistake the first couple times, but then we all started doing it, to break the boredom.

BEEP! The public announcement system came on, giving us a jump. "He's here!" someone mischievously shouted in response.

"*Masoud Kaameli, Babak Hodjat, Vahid Kashfi, and Keyhan Rafii, please come to the office now!*"

It was Mrs. Rahimi's voice. We ran as fast as we could, feeling important. Important enough to run on the soft carpets, which felt like a strange thing to be doing in a school hallway.

"Yes, Ma'am?" we all said to Mrs. Rahimi when we arrived at her office. She was surrounded with people, including two officers.

"Mr. Saadegh…" she said, pointing us toward him.

"Follow me!" Mr. Saadegh said. The smell of his cologne, mixed with his sweat, was pretty strong, and made it easier to follow him through the thick crowd that had gathered at the main entrance.

"You guys stand here," he said, stationing us at the front of the row of first graders.

"You two." He pointed at Masoud and me. "Stand on this side."

Being so much bigger than the other kids, we must have looked too conspicuous, all standing on one side together.

"OK," he said, frowning. "Don't run out, until his Royal Excellency has passed that classroom over there." He pointed. "Got it?" He looked each of us in the eye, one by one. One by one, we nodded.

"Now listen, kids!" He was suddenly shouting at the top of his voice, which was loud, giving us all another jump and quieting the whole hallway down. "We are not throwing the petals *at* His Royal Excellency." He imitated an exaggerated overhand pitch. "Not like that." There were a few nervous laughs. "We gently toss them in front of him, so he steps on them."

Mr. Saadegh looked around, rearranged a few kids, picked some lint off a rug, and hurried back to the principal's office.

We stood there for an eternity. The more we waited, the less exciting and the more exhausting the whole thing felt. Some of the kids started sitting down, and more and more of the kids got on the rugs. Some even rolled around on them. Some wrestled.

About the time when I gave up peeking out the front windows, not seeing anything happening, the bell went off. All the kids scrambled to their places. The girls straightened their dresses. The entrance doors swung open and a big crowd of suits and black ties poured in.

It was instant madness. The kids all starting to scream "Javid Shah!" at the top of their lungs and out of time with each other. The PA speakers blasted out the national anthem. The cameramen swung their equipment left and right, or hustled to new positions for better angles.

And a crowd of grown-ups made their way down the hall.

So, which one's the Shah? I thought, eager to finally discard my fistfuls of petals, but I couldn't spot him anywhere. Finally, from inside the busy crowd, I saw a tight cluster of four or five men walking at a leisurely pace. The short old bald guy in front had to be Hoveida, the former prime minister, who was now the Minister of the Court. He was famous for his pipes, and for walking with a cane. Right behind him there was a short old man with grey hair, and lots of lines on his forehead. *Is this the Shah?* He looked so familiar, yet so strangely different.

"JAVID— JAVID SHAH!! JAVID—JAV—SHAH SHAH!!" The shouts were deafening.

The petals! I tried to find a way to toss them at his feet. But there were too many people around him. *Just throw, you fool!* I thought, and opened my fists to throw them over the man in front of me, but my palm was too sweaty and the crumpled petals stuck. After a couple of tries, I managed to get rid of them, but the contingent had moved on and were already at the classroom that Mr. Saadegh had pointed to.

"Let's go!" I yelled, and Masoud, Vahid, Keyhan and I sprinted out the entrance. We dashed around the side of the school as fast as we could, pumping our arms. At the end of the carpets, where the Shah must have first stepped out of his limousine, Masoud and I bent to roll up the first rug, lift it to our shoulders, and jog it to the other side of the school without looking back.

As I smelled that hay-like scent and felt the rough fabric of the rolled-up carpet against my neck, I thought to myself that I would remember this moment for the rest of my life.

***

A few years later, during the real revolution of my time, destruction became a mode of expressing disagreement with the Shah's regime. We were teenagers then, and the huge change in society coincided with major changes in our bodies and minds. We'd still play in The Jungle, but rather than playing Cowboys and Indians, we were now into exploding things. We'd fill a cardboard box with newspapers, place the explosives inside, and light it. Cans of insecticide made a powerful noise, but properly prepared spray paint would explode with an awesome colorful mushroom cloud.

Another favorite new pastime was to make a circle of fire and toss a scorpion into it. The scorpion would follow an elaborate pattern, sort of like drawing a star, trying to find a way out, and when it finally gave up, it would go to the center, raise its tail, and bring it down on its own head, committing suicide.

Another exercise in brutality was to pluck a dragonfly's wings, set it on top of a wall for a couple of hours until it was really hungry, and then offer it its own tail to eat, which it did until it toppled over, dead.

One day, a group of us in a particularly expressive mood decided to break all the fancy lamp posts that had been installed years ago, in that rush before the Shah's visit. They had never been lit. In fact, we suspected they didn't even have any wiring installed in them. Their posts were too sturdy to break, but we did manage to break the yellow opaque lamp glass with rocks and sticks. Sure enough, they didn't even have bulbs.

"What a bunch of suck-ups!" my friend Amir shouted and shattered another lamp.

"Marg-bar Shah! Death to Shah!" Keyhan shouted.

"Some asshole in the municipality stole millions of the people's money for this bullshit!" Ali said.

"Like a bunch of clowns!"

"God, those idiots stole!" Arash said. "Remember the trees?"

The palm trees lining the boulevard leading to the airport had all died within days of the Shah's departure. We found out later that they didn't even have a chance: They had been planted as stumps in the ground, without roots.

"Yeah, I remember them! And that useless postbox." Masoud pointed.

What a great idea, we thought. Surely it would be easier to destroy than the lamps, so we got to work, but the darned thing had been cemented into the sidewalk and wouldn't budge. We managed to wedge a bar between the door and its frame, and we heaved it open, breaking the lock. It was full of garbage and dirt inside, but I spotted the side of a yellowing envelope sticking out of the filth.

"A letter!" I cried, and pulled it out.

"That's the only one," Masoud said, sifting through the rest of the dirt. "Who's it from?"

"It's hard to read," I replied. "It's all faded."

"Gimme." Amir snatched it out of my hands and squinted at it. "It's from freakin' Naazila and Naader Nayebi!" The Nayebis were one of the first families to flee Iran and emigrate to the U.S. during the revolution.

"Open it!" Ali said, and Amir tore it open.

"*Dear Grandpa,*" Amir started reading, in a mock girly voice, encouraged by our laughter. "*I hope this letter finds you well. We finally have a postbox in the Kooy, which makes it very convenient for us to send you letters. His Royal Excellency graced us with his presence last week. He visited the Kooy and our school, and we were honored and very happy. His Excellency is super intelligent. Dad says that when he visited the math department, he asked about the number of students, and calculated the number of students per square-foot at the university, all in his head, stumping the head of the department. Also, at school, one of the kids recited a poem she wrote in his honor, and he made up a beautiful verse in response. We are so lucky to have his Royal Excellency as the father of our nation. Just as the Kooy looks so beautiful and modern since his visit, our whole country is heading towards the gates of a great civilization...*"

"Aw!" Amir screamed, tossing the letter on the ground before it burned his fingers. Ali had lit it with a match. We all watched the paper crumple and turn into ash while competing in cursing the Shah, one-upping each other in vulgarity.

HORROR AT THE BLACK CASTLE

*M*asoud, Keyhan, and I were sitting around on Keyhan's porch, not having much to do. It was a nice, mild Friday in Ahwaz's university housing campus, or the Kooy, mid-Autumn, and we were eleven years old. We had just finished playing ping-pong by losing our last ball and had been thinking about what else to do. I was looking at the big circular hole in the concrete wall wondering about the legend of Kamran Miremaadi and how he had dived right through it, head-first, into the bushes, and survived without a scratch. Kamran was two years older than us and older kids were awesome.

"Let's start a secret society." Masoud said, out of the blue.

"What kind of a society?" Keyhan asked. He was always the one that seemed to need more of an explanation on everything. He was quieter than Masoud and me, maybe on account of his extrovert brother. He was also more awkward. Sort of like the Ringo to our Paul and John. Somehow, when he made a mistake, or didn't get it, it was cool and fun, while it seemed unacceptable if either of us were slow to catch on to something.

Masoud turned to him and with a somewhat patronizing tone

explained that this was to be a '*secret*' society. "We should not mention it to anyone," he cautioned, rather redundantly.

"Mention what?" Keyhan wasn't getting it again.

"The society," Masoud said. "The three of us will be the founding members."

"We'll need a place to convene our meetings." I was thinking of the old Little Lulu comics I'd inherited from my mom, and how Tubby and his friends had a club with a big 'No Girls Allowed' sign.

"You mean like a treehouse?"

"Yeah, or a tent."

"Do you have a tent, Keyhan?" Masoud asked.

"No."

"My uncle has one, but it's up north," I said. "It's pretty big. Fits four people."

"Yeah, we need something of that size." Masoud nodded. "We'd just have to buy one, then."

"We can do chores for people and raise the money," I suggested. "How much do you figure we'd need?"

"Probably a thousand tomans," Masoud said, matter-of-factly.

"Wow!" I couldn't even imagine that amount. I had only just started learning about the price of things. I knew that a pack of Rooster brand gum was five rials and so you could get two for one toman. Two thousand packs of rooster brand gum was a lot.

"What kind of chores?" Keyhan asked.

I shrugged. "You know, clean up their houses, do their shopping, clear out the leaves."

"Yeah, we can charge two tomans for every half-hour of work." Masoud had a way of making things too complicated sometimes.

"But what would we do in this society?" Keyhan still wasn't getting it.

"Anything we want!" Masoud said.

"But *secretly*," I added.

"Like what?"

"Oh, you know, we can play games between members," Masoud said.

Keyhan didn't look convinced. "But we can already play games."

"We can do good things for people," I suggested, "Secretly."

"Like what?"

"You know—projects."

"Things people need," Masoud added.

"Like help the needy?" Keyhan asked.

"Yeah," replied Masoud, and I bet the three of us started thinking about the Arab workers that did the landscaping for the Kooy and seemed to be poor.

"We can do cultural things too," I suggested.

"Yeah, like publish a newspaper," Masoud said.

"Or do a play." I said this casually, but Masoud's eyes lit up.

"Yeah!" He started jumping up and down. "We will do a comedy for the Kooy."

"We shouldn't tell anyone!" I insisted. Secrecy was even more urgently needed now that what we were doing was so important and fun. I felt butterflies in my tummy.

"We will be the Kooy's Secret Society," Masoud declared.

"The KSS!" I said. "I like it!"

"KSS," Keyhan repeated, still not completely sure what the whole thing was about.

We sat back down, contemplating the enormity of the decision. This was serious stuff. We had a mission. We felt like pioneers. As far as we knew, no one had done this before in the entire eight-year history of the Kooy. We would be famous.

"OK then," Masoud started, in an important voice, "I hereby declare the first secret meeting of the KSS adjourned." And he let out a big, noisy fart.

Keyhan and I, having not expected this at all, jumped up together on either side of Masoud, and ran away from him screaming. We both leapt through the big circular hole in the wall and into the bushes, laughing.

***

In our next meeting, we spent an hour and a half deciding on a pricing scheme and a list of chores to raise money for the tent.

"How should we market our services?" Keyhan asked.

"We can print out flyers," Masoud suggested, but we decided that was too hard. We didn't have a problem handing people flyers or sticking them on the walls. That part was easy. What was hard was actually printing them out. We couldn't use pen and paper. That would look too amateurish, plus there was a very real risk that no one could read our handwriting. Arash Azami's dad would let him use his typewriter, and Masoud and I had gotten all excited about it once, and had decided to write and publish books and become famous. Masoud had even written a five-page short story that had been forced to shrink to half a page due to typing time constraints, and even that had taken more than an hour to type by Arash, who was an expert—well, not really, he just knew how to type the word 'the' very fast. The thought of typing ten flyers like that made it completely impractical, in our minds.

Keyhan abruptly said, "How about we tell our parents and—"

"We can't tell anyone!" Masoud and I said together.

"But how can we do chores for people without telling them then?"

Keyhan had a point.

"We'll just say we're raising money for college, or to donate to the poor or something," Masoud suggested. "We're poor, so that wouldn't be a lie."

So, we told our parents, and they really loved the idea, and told their friends and neighbors, and soon the word spread, and people felt obliged to help us by giving us chores. My mom had suggested that we not set a price for the chores and to leave it up to people's best intentions.

"It's like a donation," she'd said.

"But it's not!" I had insisted. "We're working for it."

"You'll probably make more that way," she'd suggested.

We could see how that would work, and so we went with it.

"So how much would you charge me for standing in line in the morning and buying me milk?" Dr. Mohebbi had asked us that evening.

Dr. Mohebbi was one of the most charming people I knew. I felt very close to him. His face looked as if he was just about to tell a very good joke, and he was quite funny too. Always smiling, 'M' shaped hairline, raised bushy eyebrows, twinkly eyes, tiny, curled hair. His facial features must have generated an expectation of being humorous, which he totally lived up to.

"We don't charge anything," I blurted out.

"You mean it's free?"

"No! I mean we don't set a price," I said.

"It's whatever you want to pay," Masoud added.

"O...K." Dr. Mohebbi looked hesitant. "Be at my door at five tomorrow morning and I'll give you the container."

We nodded.

"Knock softly," he added, smiling.

Getting up at 5 a.m. was not a problem. We were both excited about the new job and were ready and at Dr. Mohebbi's door at 4:45, whispering about our KSS plans, and the tent, and the play, and pretty much everything except what was really on our minds: how much would he pay?

The door swung open suddenly. "You guys are early!" Dr. Mohebbi exclaimed in a hushed voice.

"I hope we didn't wake you up," I said, as Dr. Mohebbi handed me the large plastic container and some money.

"Two gallons." He pointed at the neck of the container. "It should fill up to here."

There was a line of four or five groggy customers at Berenji's already by the time we got there. Mr. Berenji pretty much had a monopoly on commerce at the Kooy as he had the only store on the university campus and within five kilometers. People complained about how he was too expensive and there were rumors of him being dishonest, like mixing water with milk, but I'm not sure how much of that was real and how much was just the general mistrust of business that prevailed during the early post-revolution days.

"Two gallons, please," I said and handed him the money.

After standing in line for what felt like an eternity, it was finally our turn.

He started filling the container. "You're Dr. Hodjat's son, are you?"

"Yeah."

"Dr. Kaameli?" he asked, pointing at Masoud.

Masoud nodded.

"Good boys! Giving your parents a hand. Good boys!" He smiled and placed the full container in front of me to take.

I smiled back and picked it up, but the handle was wet and it slipped out of my hand, leaving the container unmoved.

"Careful. It's a bit heavy."

So Masoud and I picked the container up together and heaved our way out of the store as quickly as we could so no one would notice how we were struggling with the weight of the thing. We set it down as soon as we were out the door.

"Goddamn it, that's heavy!" I said.

"Yeah, wasn't heavy when it was empty, was it?" Masoud looked annoyed.

"Well, I brought it all the way to the store, so you're taking it back,"

I retorted.

"Sure," Masoud replied, sarcastically.

"How about we carry it in our arms?" I tried picking it up, but it was as if the container was designed to make it hard to carry.

"It's like a gold bullion," I joked. "Im… po…ssi…ble to move!" I set it down again.

We kept picking it up, walking a few steps, and setting it back down again to catch our breath. It took us a full half hour to get back to Dr. Mohebbi's house, which was on the second floor, and another ten minutes to take it up the stairs, step by step. By the time we rang Dr. Mohebbi's doorbell, the handle on the container had left stripe marks on our palms, and our backs hurt.

"Didn't I tell you to knock softly?" Dr. Mohebbi asked in a loud hush.

"So sorry!" I said.

"OK. Wait a moment." Dr. Mohebbi took the container inside and shut the door behind him.

So, we waited…

And waited…

And waited…

"What did he say?" I wondered if I had misheard something.

"I think he said to wait a moment."

"That's what I thought too."

We didn't dare knock.

"I haven't had breakfast," Masoud said.

"Yeah. And I need to pee real bad."

"Maybe he went back to bed?"

The door opened, finally.

"Sorry guys, I had to bottle the milk and put it in the fridge." He handed me an envelope. "Thanks a lot, guys. See you again next Monday at five?"

"Sure!" I was all excited with anticipation for finding out what was in that envelope and had completely forgotten the hardship we'd just gone through.

We ran down the stairs through the perimeter bush around Masoud's backyard and onto their porch as fast as we could. I opened the envelope.

"I can't believe it!" I said as I looked inside.

"How much is it?"

"Five rials!" I held the coin up. All that, for a single pack of Rooster brand gum!

***

Unbeknownst to us, our parents, had told other Kooy residents not to overpay. Maybe they didn't trust us with too much money and were concerned that people, finding what we're doing charming, would become too generous. Maybe they wanted us to learn the true meaning of 'hard earned cash.' Whatever the reason, at the end of the first week of grass cutting, babysitting, tutoring, and car washing, we had collected a discouraging total of five tomans.

"At this rate we'd have to work for five years to collect a thousand tomans," I said.

We sat there for a while, staring at the pile of coins and pondering.

"We should do the play," Masoud said, finally.

"Yeah," Keyhan added. "We can have our secret meetings on our porch for now."

"Yeah. No more chores. It's bad for my health."

"What about Dr. Mosadegh's then?"

Dr. Mosadegh was our upstairs neighbor and he had called us over to do some chores that evening.

"That's the last one," declared Masoud.

That night Dr. Mosadegh opened the door on me and Masoud with a big smile. "Welcome! Come on in, boys."

We worked hard, vacuuming and dusting and moving his furniture around. At the end though, as it turned out, Dr. Mosadegh had not gotten the memo, or he'd chosen to ignore it, or maybe he simply had a different standard than the others. When we were done, he treated us to some fish-fingers, which were very tasty, and gave us each a five toman bill on the way out.

We couldn't believe it. We felt rich and hopeful and loved people again, and wanted to spend the rest of our lives doing chores for them.

"Awesome!"

"I don't know about you, but I'd do chores for Dr. Mosadegh any time."

"So would I!"

"He paid us double what we made all week!"

"I know!"

"At this rate we'd have a tent sometime late next year!"

"We should set it up in the forest behind the big houses."

"There are scorpions there."

"We'll light a fire." We remembered how scorpions don't like fire.

"We can make more money if we have more members."

"No!" Masoud said. "It should remain secret."

"But what about Amir Attari or Massih Tadayon? What if they want to join?"

"They're too old and busy chasing girls all the time."

They were one year older than us, which was a lot. But it was true that their priorities had shifted lately and they were less fun than they used to be, insisting on playing hide-and-seek with the girls, which was fine, but then being distracted by the girls while we played, which was totally uncool.

"Let's do the play first," Masoud said.

"OK."

"Let's meet at my place tomorrow and work on it." Masoud smiled. "I already have a sketch for the story."

"What's it about?"

"Horror at the Black Castle."

"That's a great name!"

"Yeah. I'll be the playwright."

"We don't have to type it, do we?"

"No," Masoud said, quickly. "We'll just write it down in a notebook for our own use."

I thought about it for a moment. "Sounds good. I'll be the director."

***

We worked on the screenplay for a few days, and it came out pretty funny. It chronicled the adventures of a student who receives a letter from an uncle he never knew existed and ends up at his scary castle. I think, subconsciously, we'd been influenced by the Mel Brooks comedies of the day, like *Young Frankenstein* and *Silent Movie*, and the play was a collection of gags and slapstick.

Masoud cast himself as the scary uncle, who was a surgeon by profession. Keyhan was cast as the lead role, and I was the lead's best friend, a cool dude who was afraid of nothing and who was called into the castle by Keyhan to keep him company. I thought of my character as The Fonz and loved the fact that my first appearance wasn't until the fifth scene.

After pitching the story to Keyhan in our first practice session, we redid much of the play.

One of the problems we ran into was that Keyhan had a hard time keeping a straight face. His timing was also off.

In one of the earlier scenes, Masoud, after pacing around Keyhan, was supposed to turn to him suddenly and ask: "So you are my brother's son?" and Keyhan was to fall off his chair backwards. We must have practiced it more than twenty times, but he was either too quick, or too slow, or too awkward, or—more often than not—too busy laughing to pull it off. It didn't help that Masoud jumbled the words once: "So mew high by mother's son?" which made us all fall to the floor, laughing.

That was it. We had the laughs now and there was no way of controlling it. We'd swear to keep it serious and all frown, and that would make things even funnier when one of us cracked up.

"OK guys, come on! We've got to get this right. It's just the second scene," Masoud pleaded.

"Yeah, OK. Let's do it," I said.

"Let's do it!" Keyhan added.

So Masoud paced around Keyhan's chair a couple of times and turned towards him suddenly, but before he could say anything...

"What's a 'mew high' anyway?" Keyhan asked, right on cue this time, and we all exploded with laughter.

Walking home with Masoud that evening, I was very concerned. We'd run through two or three scenes, but it had been a disaster. I mean, it was fun and we laughed a lot, but I'd lost all hope that the play would ever become a reality that way.

"This isn't working," I said.

"No," Masoud said, thoughtfully.

"Keyhan's a great guy, but he's not good for this role."

Masoud shook his head. "But he has to be part of it. He's in the KSS. Maybe I should play the lead and we can have him play the uncle."

"The uncle has a lot of words too. Keyhan's not good at words."

"How about we add a character for him, like a scary butler or something?" Masoud suggested.

"Yeah! A scary butler with single-word dialogs." Maybe the play was not doomed after all. "We'll have him hold a candle at all times and walk really slowly, with a blanket on his head."

I went to bed happy that night. We'd come up with a great solution, and the play would be even funnier for it. But suddenly, it struck me. We had a problem! I jumped out of bed and ran to the living room.

"I need to call Masoud."

"No! It's too late for that," Mom said.

"But it's really important!"

"Weren't you with him just now? I'm sure it can wait till tomorrow."

"Mom!"

She must have seen the look of desperation on my face, so she agreed. "Make it quick then."

And I dialed, 30980.

"Hello?"

"May I speak with Masoud, please?"

"Sure, Babak-jaan, hold on…"

"Hello?" came Masoud's voice from the other end.

"Masoud," I said, desperately, "who's gonna play the lead?"

***

We decided it was OK to tell a few people what we were up to; without mentioning the secret club, of course.

We had to tell our parents. Mom was quite helpful. She suggested that my dad speak to the daycare principal to see if we could use their space as the venue. Masoud's dad suggested we hold an audition for the lead role, and we told a few of the kids we thought might be suitable.

Sepehr seemed to be a good choice. He was a great volleyball player and had taught us how to play. He was cool, good-looking and confident. The problem, though, was that he was too soft-spoken for the role. He simply had no 'loud' on his volume nob and nobody would hear him. Plus, he lived in a housing complex twenty minutes away from the Kooy and was not always available.

We reluctantly let Sassan audition. He was two years younger than us, and so we didn't really play with him much or know him that well, other than the fact that he was Suzy's little brother and Suzy was OK. To our surprise, we found that Sassan was a good actor and fit the role well. Being younger than us, it was a great privilege for him to be part of this project, and so he worked hard and took it seriously. This encouraged us and we gave him the role.

After a few more weeks of practicing, we were ready. The daycare folks agreed to let us use their facilities and we went to check the place out with my parents. This was one of the large homes in the Kooy that had been repurposed as a daycare. The principal was one of the Kooy residents and she had seen us many times in the neighborhood and was very kind to us.

"It's so great what you guys are doing. Are you Dr. Kaameli's son?" she asked Masoud.

Masoud nodded.

"You guys have grown so big! Your parents must be proud of you."

She pointed at the living room area, "You can clear this area out and move the toys and stuff to the back. When is your play?"

"Next weekend," I replied.

"You guys can use anything you want here," she said. "Just put it back to its original state after you're done."

She smiled at us and paused for a few seconds, probably thinking of her own childhood, or dreaming about her own children. Then she snapped out of it with a start, remembering something.

"Oh! Just one thing," she said with a serious face. "Don't scratch the walls."

She turned to my mom and explained, apologetically, "They can do all they want with the furniture. We rent this house and the landlord is very particular about the walls."

The place was great. The living room was large. We could use the front half as the seating area and the stage would be what must have been the adjacent dining room. There was a side door to the kitchen in the back where there was a door to the backyard. We could use the kitchen as the backstage.

"Don't worry," my mom said to the principal, "we'll make sure the place is tidied up and cleaned after the show."

"You can get the keys from me Thursday evening." The principal gave me a big smile.

We headed out, excited and energized. It was really happening.

"We should practice every day," Masoud said. "Keyhan needs to stop smiling."

"Yeah." He was right. We couldn't afford to screw it up now. "And Sassan still stutters on some of his longer dialogs."

"We need props."

"Yeah. Let's go to my place and make a list."

"We need to practice," Masoud repeated.

"Every day."

***

We became obsessed with the play, so much so that our parents got a bit worried. The last few days were particularly hard. I was too excited and couldn't sleep well. Masoud had lost his appetite and was only convinced to eat after his parents threatened to scrap the whole project.

We got our little brothers and their friends to help with the flyers and tickets. Per Mom's insistence, we didn't put a price on the tickets. It simply read: "Price: up to your best intentions."

Mom made us a curtain out of some blankets and a big rope to hold it up. I borrowed Amir Attari's black leather jacket for my role, promising to give him my skateboard if I put a scratch on it. Jimi gave me a pair of cool sunglasses to go with it. They were a bit large for me, and too dark to use indoors, but they were great. I spent a whole afternoon listening to my parents' records to find something for the scene where I was to be playing loud music and singing, ignorant of the scary events in the play that were happening in the background. I finally picked a James Brown for the screaming. Masoud found an old smoking pipe and a Sherlock Holmes cap for his role.

The only prop we bought was a ping-pong ball. I'm not quite sure why we couldn't find a single ping-pong ball in the Kooy, but we really needed one, and so we used some of the tent money to get a pack (they didn't sell them individually). The ball was to be used as Sassan's eye during the surgery.

We also got some cotton balls for the white liver. This was a joke that Masoud had come up with for the surgery scene. Masoud was to perform surgery on Sassan's eye to restore his eyesight but would cut his belly open instead. He'd then pull out the cotton ball, I'd ask him what that was, and he'd say, "It's the white liver, of course." He laughed so hard when he came up with the joke that we laughed along. It was the scene everyone laughed the hardest at in every practice run, and I laughed too, even though I didn't understand why it was funny.

That Thursday evening the daycare principal was stunned to find us waiting for the last kid to be picked up and for her to give us the keys.

She looked at the many chairs and props that we had spent the entire afternoon hauling up to the sidewalk in front of the daycare and said, "All this is for the play?"

We nodded.

"Here you go." She handed me the keys. "Are you sure you don't need help?"

"No, thank you," we said as we waited impatiently for her to get in her car and leave, before running to open the front door.

There were lots of toys and kiddie desks and arts and crafts equipment all over the place. We cleared out everything in the living room, moving them to the bedrooms. We even moved stuff into the bathroom. We found a broom and swept the living room before moving the chairs in. We lined the two front rows with cushions and pillows so the smaller kids could sit.

Putting the curtain up was somewhat challenging. We tied a rope around a column but had no place to tie the other side, so I hammered a sizable pin to the opposite wall and tightened the other end of the rope to it. The curtain opened in the middle and we had carefully choreographed the play so an actor would exit on either side at the end of each scene, and pull the curtains shut.

We worked on the place until eleven p.m. and had to be dragged out by our parents to go home. None of us slept that night.

***

My worries grew exponentially on the day of the play. *What if nobody shows up? What if they don't like the play? What if we screw up? What if Keyhan's not funny?*

That morning, I walked through the entire play several times in my head. No one made a mistake, the costumes where perfect, and Keyhan actually looked like Marty Feldman. But there was something wrong. It was too scripted. The jokes were tired and the timing was off.

I had to find Masoud.

I ran into him and Keyhan in front of Keyhan's house. They'd just gotten back from Berenji's and were carrying a box.

"What's that?" I asked.

"Candy," Masoud explained. "We're going to sell it during the play."

"We're getting ice cream too," Keyhan added proudly.

"Yeah, we'll bring that right before the play so it doesn't melt," Masoud said.

"You're going to sell stuff?" I asked. Something felt wrong about this whole affair.

"Yeah." Masoud threw up his shoulders, looking at me with an awkward smile.

"We borrowed the money from our parents," Keyhan said.

"We're marking the candy up by five rials and the ice cream by a toman." Masoud smiled. "We'll make a healthy profit."

"You want to partner with us?" Keyhan asked.

"No!" I was a bit offended that they had not offered me a partnership earlier, but that was not the main source of my disgruntlement. "You guys want to make a profit off of the play?"

"Yeah," Keyhan said, with a smile, probably not reading my feelings well.

"What's wrong with that?" Masoud asked.

I frowned. "I thought we were doing this for the good of our community. I didn't think of it as a business."

"Well, we are," Masoud said. "But what's wrong with making money?"

"It dilutes our goal. Makes the whole thing seem... seem... commercial!" I couldn't hold back my frustration.

"Look," Masoud said, frowning now, "it's hot. They're gonna want ice cream. We're carrying it all the way from Berenji's. That's gotta be worth something?"

I guess he had a point, but I still wasn't convinced. I thought about it for a moment and decided, finally, that I had made my objection known and the subject didn't deserve more debate.

"When should we do our dress rehearsal?" I asked.

***

By all measures, the play was a huge success. The place got so full of people some folks couldn't even get in. There were people standing in the back and on the sides, and even a few rows of standing in the doorway hall. All the candy and ice cream were sold out before the play even started.

And people laughed.

I mean, they really laughed. Not a polite, oh-look-how-sweet kind of laugh. No. It was an oh-my-God-this-is-hilarious kind of side-splitting laughter. We got it right: the acting, the dialogs, the timing, the slapstick, the deadpan, the double-takes, the stumbles, the punchlines. Keyhan's scary butler was just right. Masoud had just the right mix of mad and scientist in his character. Sassan's dead-serious-and-completely-naïve was perfect, and he got one of the biggest laughs in the third scene the way he fell off the chair. We found out later that he'd come down a bit harder than he should have and hurt his butt in the process, but that he had hidden his pain through the play. He said it helped him with his acting.

I utterly enjoyed the confusion in the audience during the first five acts before I actually entered the play. I was standing next to one of the side walls, listening and pretending not to hear people speculate.

"Isn't Babak in the play?"

"He's got to be. I thought he was part of the gang."

"Maybe he's the director."

In my song and dance scene, I lip-synced and danced without inhibition to the James Brown song. My secret to doing that scene well was to concentrate on the girls in the audience whom I really wanted to impress and block out any thoughts of the grown-ups and teachers that may have been watching in the blur of heads and eyes in front of me.

The white-liver joke in the surgery scene got a good number of laughs, too. To this day, I still don't know what was funny about the joke. What's a white liver anyway?

Even the curtain was a success. There were some oohs and aahs from some of the kids in the audience every time the curtain magically closed or opened. They couldn't quite figure out the mechanism, I guess.

At the end of one of the final scenes, Keyhan and I had exited on either side and were pulling the curtains shut, when the audience suddenly fell utterly silent for a few seconds. The rope had somehow broken loose and Keyhan and I were just standing there, exposed and still holding the tip of the curtains up in our hands.

We looked at each other and I saw terror in Keyhan's face, but I stayed in character. "Dude! Who needs this anyway?" I tossed the curtain on the ground and walked backstage with a pronounced swagger. Keyhan looked at the curtain in his hand, shrugged, tossed it too, and slowly made his way out.

The audience exploded with laughter and applause. I was so proud of Keyhan, I would have hugged him had it not been uncool to hug another guy. I described what had just happened to Masoud and Sassan who'd been in the kitchen all along, and Masoud high-fived us both. "Good job!"

The final scene came naturally to us. We were full of self-confidence now, partly because we knew we could trust each other not to screw up. The audience was eating our every move and word and laughing at everything, even if it wasn't supposed to be funny.

At the end, the applause was long and deafening, and we came out to bow a couple of times. Everyone seemed to have enjoyed themselves thoroughly and came up to congratulate us on a job well done. It took people quite a while to file out.

"We killed it!" Masoud said, with a big smile.

"It was awesome!"

"Good job, Sassan, Keyhan. You guys were great!"

We didn't have much time for celebration though. It was getting late and we had to clear the place out and clean it up. The kindergarten was to open the next morning, so we all went to work. I started folding the chairs and carrying them out.

"Babak!" Masoud called suddenly, with some alarm in his voice.

"What?" I turned and found him looking down at something. Keyhan and Sassan came over too.

It was the large pin I'd used to secure the curtain to the wall. It was lying there on the ground, with a great big chunk of the wall plaster still attached to it. We all raised our heads slowly and looked up at the place on the wall where it came from. It was ugly. At least three rows of bricks were showing.

"Didn't she say, 'don't scratch the walls'?" Masoud asked.

"That's some scratch," Sassan said.

"They're never gonna let us use this place again." Keyhan shook his head.

We stood there silently for a few seconds.

"Whatever!" Masoud clearly didn't want this to ruin the night. "Our next venue is Broadway anyway."

We all laughed, and right then I had an idea. I ran to the bathroom and found a big tube of toothpaste that must have belonged to one of the teachers. Within minutes, I had the plaster back in place, and I'd even taken the pin out and filled the hole.

"Cool!" The guys were impressed.

"Do you guys see a scratch?" I boasted.

"Scratch? What scratch?" Masoud asked, and we high-fived again.

WAR

*T*he war was not a sudden lightening shock that changed everything instantaneously. It was much more gradual than that. It did change everything, though.

I was eleven, about to turn twelve in a couple of months, already starting to make a wish-list in my head for my birthday presents. A volleyball would be nice.

We were enjoying the last days of the summer holidays in the Kooy and, with most of the kids having returned from their summer vacations, we were trying to make the most of the few days we had before start of school, first day of fall. We had just finished a soccer tournament we had organized ourselves, and we were playing a lot of volleyball.

I came home from the schoolyard one day to find Dad pacing around the room, carrying my colicky baby sister, Sara, and Mom shouting into the telephone. She smiled at me as I looked inquiringly, but she seemed to be worried.

"We are fine. Are *you* OK?" she was asking on the phone.

"She's talking to your grandmother, Maman Bahram," explained my dad. "Something about bombings in Tehran." It was hard to hear the conversation over Sara's wailing.

"Bombings?"

At first, I thought it must be a terrorist attack. We'd had some of those lately. The Islamic regime was consolidating its power, and groups that were left out, mainly leftists, had started to take up arms to reclaim what they thought to be *their* revolution.

"Iraqi warplanes have raided Tehran," Mom said to us after she hung up. She took Sara from my dad and continued with a chuckle, "Maman was worried about us. I told her everything is OK *here*."

We lived in Ahwaz, the capital of the oil-rich province of Khuzestan, in the south west. Saddam started the war to annex Khuzestan to Iraq, but the first strikes were on Tehran.

"They tried to bomb the airport, but Maman says they missed."

***

War. You see a lot of it in movies and in the news, but an actual war unfolds like a mystery. At every step of the way, for the first few years, most people expected the war to end soon. Most people didn't expect things to get worse. There was a lot of hope in our circles. My parents and their friends were educated, Westernized, and successful. There's a certain naiveté that comes along with that success.

There were no strikes on Ahwaz for a few days after that phone call. We did get news of air raids on some other major cities, but life went on as normal for us. My parents stayed glued to the news. We had a motorized antenna on the roof and, pointing it to the south, we could watch Kuwait TV, which had English-language news. With the state-owned media being full of rhetoric and slogans, people trusted them less and were getting their news from multiple sources and making their own minds up. The most popular radio sources were the BBC's Persian service, followed by VOA and Radio Israel.

Mom bought paper duct tape and we taped all the windows: covering the sides with a square and taping an X through the middle to minimize injuries from shattering glass. She also prepared a supplies bag with some food and first aid.

"This is all just in case," she kept saying. "It will never get to this, but better safe than sorry."

We were playing volleyball in the schoolyard one afternoon when my dad and a bunch of the professors showed up with a pail of mud.

"There's a bright and shiny water storage tank on top of the school building." Dad pointed. "We're going to cover it in mud so you guys stay safe from enemy air raids."

I didn't quite understand that explanation, but they were grown-ups and knew better.

They worked on it for a good hour, but I'm not sure how much of the mud actually got on the tank. When we got home, Mom forced Dad to take most of his muddy clothes off at the door and go straight to the shower.

After a few days, though, the air raids on Ahwaz started too. You'd hear the loud whoosh of the fighter jet first, Russian Migs, followed shortly thereafter by anti-aircraft and machine gun shots. Then, usually, a loud explosion or two, or maybe the second one was just the echo, and then a couple of minutes later, silence, with people browsing the horizon for smokestacks marking where a bomb had landed.

A few minutes later, the air raid sirens would go off on all the radios and mosque loudspeakers announcing red alert, which started with a relatively indifferent male voice saying, *'Attention! Attention! The sound you are about to hear is the red alert siren and it means that an enemy air raid is underway or imminent. Please take shelter.'*

The first few times, of course, we all took the sirens very seriously and ran to shelter. Mom had put cushions and pillows under the dining table, and some on it, and we'd run under there, lie down, and place a pillow on our heads until the white alert siren signaled the end of the attack. I guess it was more of a psychological shelter than anything else, the pillows acting more as a kind of security blanket.

I didn't like it there at all. I would have much preferred to be in my mom's embrace, but for some reason she never joined us under the table. We later learned that the safest place to take shelter is in the archway of doors, or under a stairway.

After a while, though, we learned to treat the red alert sirens as more of a relief and something of a dark joke, signaling the end of the raid. It was only much later in the war, five or six years into it, when the sirens actually signaled an imminent attack. By then they'd either acquired a better radar system or learned to plant lookouts on hills to spot the incoming scud missiles.

After two or three days of this, we learned other patterns too. For instance, the air raids never happened at night. In fact, it seemed like we got three a day, usually around mealtimes. Many of the raids were targeting Ahwaz's famous suspension bridge over the Karoun River. They missed every time, which made it scarier. In fact, the bridge was never hit during the eight-year war, but plenty of stores around it on each side were destroyed.

There was an international bookseller where we bought all our comic books and *Tintins*, right past the bridge on the other side. Keyhan and his family were returning from shopping there on the fourth day of the war and were actually on the bridge when the store was hit and destroyed. Keyhan sadly showed us the *Batman* comic he'd bought that day and we looked at it as a precious relic. Where would we buy our comics now? This war thing was starting to get really annoying.

On one occasion, my brother Siamak and I were talking to my friend Masoud at the door when we heard fighter jets. We instinctively ran to take shelter under the dining table, but Masoud didn't follow. A dogfight was going on up in the air and he started narrating it excitedly through the doorway. Eventually our embarrassment overcame our fright and we joined Masoud at the door. Mom was there already anyway.

"The Phantom F-4 has a lock on the Mig!"

"It's gonna shoot the bastard out of the sky!"

"What's that!?"

"Did the pilot parachute out?"

"Don't know. It's too far."

"It must be napalm," Masoud suggested, knowingly.

"Oh no!" We knew by now that napalms had chutes. "What if it's blown this way?"

"It would kill everyone within a kilometer radius." Masoud pretended to know.

But the planes and the parachute disappeared, and after ten or so minutes of waiting and not hearing any explosions, we decided that it had probably been the pilot and went back home to look for our toy binoculars so we'd have them handy for the next raid, which we were pretty sure would be on schedule, that evening.

***

The war was a curiosity that would end soon, we were all pretty sure of that.

This is the twentieth century, I thought. *Countries don't simply wage war to conquer other countries anymore. There are international laws, the United Nations, the civilized world. The powers that be are surely working on putting a stop to this. It's just a matter of time.*

This being the prevalent sentiment, we went on with life as usual, accepting the daily air raids as a new fact of life, and ignoring signs pointing at things getting worse.

Schools started a few days late that year, which was great. When they finally did open, a week into the fall, we stood in line for our first assembly, listening to the new principal's welcome message. Unlike last year, the program had started with a recital of some Koranic verses followed by a prayer, which included wishing safety upon our brave defenders and damnation upon Saddam.

"In the name of Allah, the compassionate, the merciful," the principal began. "You boys and girls, my little brothers and sisters, standing here, represent a strong punch to the mouth of Zionism, imperialism, communism, and their crony, Saddam Hussein. Your bravery in the face of this imposed war…" He went on and on for a good twenty minutes.

I looked around trying to spot my friends. At one point, in the middle of the speech, a school bus pulled up and a bunch of kids with shaved heads and what seemed to be ragged clothes poured out into the schoolyard.

"Let us all welcome your new friends from Ahwaz's poorest neighborhood. They will be joining us at our school this year…" the principal was saying.

We finally marched into our classes, rushing to pick the best seats, wondering what eighth grade was all about. Masoud and I had finally reunited in the same class after three years and, of course, we sat together. In the midst of the chaos, there was a sudden silence signaling the presence of a grown-up at the door. It was one of the new vice-principals.

"As of this year," she said, "boys will sit on the left side of the aisle, and girls on the right."

"What?" There were several objections, mostly by the girls, who didn't want to sit next to the boys anyway, but were not happy with the edict all the same.

"We live in an Islamic country now," the vice-principal explained sternly, and left to give the message to the next classroom.

There were still complaining noises being made on both sides of the aisle when Mr. Jahanbakhsh, our beloved literature teacher, walked in. He was a writer; we'd all read his books, and he was very charming and knowledgeable.

"Mr. Jahanbakhsh, they are forcing us to sit apart!" said one of the more vocal girls.

"This is tyrannical!" another one said.

Mr. Jahanbakhsh simply smiled and invited everyone to sit down. It was a sort of sad and helpless smile, and we knew what it meant.

"This is the first day of school and a lot has happened since last year," he began. "I'd like for us to start our class this year with an open debate. The subject of the debate is…" he paused and looked around the class, then continued. "Have things improved or gotten worse since the start of school last year?"

It was a provocative subject. Many of us were still quite bullish about the revolution and had chosen to ignore some of the recent restrictions and crackdowns, or explained them to ourselves as inevitable or necessary. But there certainly had been many changes.

"We weren't forced to sit apart from the boys last year," said one of the more vocal girls, sarcastically.

"We live in an Islamic country now," parroted one of the boys, which made everyone laugh.

"There's less freedom all around, that's for sure," one of the boys said.

"In what way?" asked the teacher.

"Well, they just shut down a bunch of newspapers and magazines for no reason."

"That's 'cause they were traitors," Masoud said, matter-of-factly.

"How can a magazine be a traitor?" I asked, genuinely curious.

"They published pictures of our oil pipelines inviting the terrorists to bomb them!" Masoud said, raising his voice a bit.

"Really?" I simply couldn't believe it and was surprised.

"Yeah," he insisted.

"That is so untrue!" one of the girls responded. "They did no such thing."

"They wrote articles against the Mullahs," someone said with a smirk.

Suddenly, a loud whoosh interrupted the whole debate.

"Air raid! Air raid!" the kids started shouting and the girls began to scream, which was very annoying.

"Let's get out of here." We were on the unsafe second floor.

Everyone started running through the door, but Masoud tapped my shoulder. I turned and saw one of the boys going through the window, and Masoud and I did the same. We jumped on a mound of dirt and began looking for the planes in the sky.

"It's the daily bridge run!" one of the kids was shouting excitedly, pointing north towards the Karoun.

The bell went off.

"School is out! School is out!" the kids shouted, and we ran home, half-frightened by the prospect of an air raid in progress, half-wanting to get home before anyone changed their minds about school being out.

***

Schools stayed closed the following day and we had our usual three courses of air raids. That evening, Mom invited a number of our Kooy neighbors over to form a civilian relief team. Dad and some of his colleagues had signed up as volunteers but were told that they were needed more in the educational 'front' than on the battlegrounds. That had inspired Mom to call up this meeting.

"We should prepare to host our soldiers," Mom had said, "and form a first aid group to tend to casualties."

"Come off it, Mrs. Hodjat," said Dr. Kaveh, one of my dad's colleagues. "This whole thing is going to be over in a few days."

"I've heard that the US has already sent its warships to the Persian Gulf," another agreed. "They're not going to let this go on. It's just a maneuver."

"OK," Mom said, "I think so too, but we should be prepared all the same."

They made a list of first aid supplies to buy and assigned responsibilities. That night, we all went to bed proud that we were doing our part to help defend our beloved country. We had no premonitions that our perspectives on the situation would change so drastically—as early as the very next morning.

***

Boom!

I woke up worried. Must be the morning air raid, I thought, but the sound was a bit different. More like a big dry funeral drum. Had I missed the whoosh?

Boom!

Maybe there's more than one plane. I decided to lie in bed a little longer until it was done.

Boom! Boom!

Boom!

Why weren't any anti-aircraft guns going off?

Boom!

Whiz! Boom!

The windows shook.

Boom!

Why wasn't this thing ending?

I put my clothes on quickly and washed my face, making a silly face at my younger brother Siamak, or Sia, who was looking at me wide-eyed. He gave me a nervous smile.

My parents were in the kitchen sitting at the breakfast table with the local radio station on louder than usual, playing military music.

Boom!

"Is this an air raid?" I asked, knowing that it couldn't be.

"Shelling," Dad said, feeding little, blissfully ignorant Sara, who was in her highchair.

"What does that mean?" asked Siamak.

"Don't worry, Sia-jaan," Mom said, with a fake smile, "it's not close to us."

"It's ground forces firing big guns," Dad went on.

"Our ground forces, very likely," Mom added.

"Yay!" Sia said. "They're kicking Saddam's butt!"

Whiz! Boom!

My expression must have fed off of Mom's pale face, and Dad picked up on it. "We are not a military target." He was trying hard to sound reassuring.

He picked up Siamak and sat him on his lap. "It's loud and scary," he said, "but it's really far away."

Boom!

"*Brothers and Sisters!*" The radio suddenly blared over the military march that had been playing all morning. We all fell silent and listened. "*Residents of the cradle of martyrdom, Ahwaz, please pay attention…*"

Dad turned the radio to face him.

Boom!

"*Please pay attention to an important message from the honorable mayor of Ahwaz…*"

Mom looked at Dad nervously, then looked at us.

"Eat up, guys. Would you like more toast?" But we were not hungry at all.

Boom! Boom!

"*In the name of God, the compassionate, the merciful,*" started the mayor, and he continued with some Arabic prayer that we didn't understand.

"For God's sake, get to it!" Dad was anxious.

"They think the Arabic makes them sound more important," Mom said.

Boom!

"*My Ahwazi Brothers and Sisters…*" Was the mayor's voice shaky, or was that just the radio?

"*As you know, we are in an unwanted war with the satanic aggressor, Saddam. I have full confidence that you, brave people of Ahwaz, will not allow an inch of our holy city to be occupied by the infidels.*"

"This can't be good," Dad said under his breath, but was shushed by Mom.

"*One hundred and fifty enemy tanks have broken through our defensive lines and are heading towards Ahwaz…*" His voice suddenly sounded to me like it was coming out of an echo chamber.

Boom!

"*We rely on God almighty and the bravery of you, the people, to defend our beloved city…*"

"What did he say?" Mom asked, frowning intently.

"Shhh!"

Boom!

"*…I will now turn the microphone over to Brother Jaarihaani who will teach you how to make Molotov cocktails…*"

Of course, by now I knew well what a Molotov cocktail was, but it took me a while to comprehend what was going on. I was still reviewing everything in my head when Mom got up with a sudden move, turned the radio off, and said, "That's it! We need to leave!"

We all jumped.

Whiz! Boom!

"Kids, go to your rooms and get your school bags and pack them with whatever you will need for the next few days." She then turned to Dad. "Let's go!"

"Where?"

Boom! Boom!

"I don't know, but let's just go."

I ran into our room. I wanted to get out of there as soon as possible. The Kooy was on the west side of the city, closer to the Iraqi border. We were close to the tanks, and they were coming at us, all one hundred and fifty of them. There was nothing between them and us. I felt like I had to go to the toilet but there was no time. What I wanted most was just to get out of there, now.

I hurriedly packed some of my schoolbooks, my camera and album, my diary from the year we lived in London, and the notebook with the beginnings of our new KSS play outlined in it. As I left the room, a thought came into my head and I ran back, took all the schoolbooks out, and instead packed my backgammon set along with a couple of *Tintins* I hadn't reread for a while. I figured I'd have a good excuse for having 'forgotten' my schoolbooks. I was a war refugee now.

The sun was very bright that day. So bright, it was hurting my eyes as we walked to the car. We ran into Dr. Mohebbi and Dr. Kaveh in the parking.

Boom!

"You guys got the mayor's message too?" Dr. Mohebbi asked, smiling sarcastically.

"Where should we go?" Dad asked him.

Boom! Boom!

"Let's go to the main agriculture department building," Dr. Mohebbi replied. "They just completed a reinforced concrete silo we can use as a shelter until this thing blows over."

Boom!

I was very frightened. I kept looking around to see if I could spot any of the shells, but I couldn't, and somehow that made it scarier. As our car turned onto the main street, I saw Masoud and his little brother, Kaivan, leaning against a wall, watching the convoy of cars leaving the Kooy. I didn't quite see the expression on their faces, but they did not seem happy. I had no idea at that moment that I would not see my best friend again for two years; and that when I finally did, he and I would be two completely different people.

***

The guard at the agriculture department unlocked the door to a building. Inside, there was a big empty hall, with what looked like a trapdoor in the middle of the floor. We all stood around it as the guard unlocked and heaved it open. The floor was indeed made of concrete, one meter thick, and the tip of a wooden ladder leaned against the edge of the dark hole into the silo.

Boom!

Dr. Mohebbi pointed at Negar, his three-year-old daughter. "Negar-jaan, you and I go in first, dear." He picked her up and walked down the ladder, slowly, looking down as he took each step. Negar's silent, frightened, wide eyes stared out at us. Her look was haunting.

Mom broke the silence. "I'm not going in there!"

"It's safe." Dr. Mohebbi's voice came from somewhere in the dark hole. "Just need to find the light."

"There ain't no light," the guard said, with an amused look on his face. Locals had a certain rhythm to their talking.

"Is this the only way through?" Dr. Kaveh asked him.

"Uh-huh."

"What if a shell falls on the building? It'll cover this hole and we'd be buried alive," Dad said.

"I'm not going in there," Mom said again, holding Sara tightly, and looking down.

Boom! Boom!

"Is this safe?" Mrs. Kaveh asked the guard. He seemed to have all the answers.

"Nope." He lingered on the 'N.'

Boom!

The guy looked really cool and collected, given the circumstances. He was leaning on one knee, chewing a piece of straw. He had squinting eyes and a sunburnt face full of lines. His head was covered by a dirty white keffiyeh.

"Where's the safest place to be during the shelling?" someone asked him.

"In the jungle," he said.

"Jungle?"

Whiz! Boom!

"Yeah." He nodded, knowingly. "Open air, 'tween trees."

"We can go to the little forest on the east side of the university," Dr. Kaveh suggested as we all headed to the cars again.

"Where are you guys going?" asked Dr. Sehat. He was driving the lead car in another convoy heading out of the Kooy and he'd seen us walking out.

***

By the time we got to the 'jungle' there must have been thirty of us. We picked a clearing, a few hundred yards in, and the ladies started setting up shop for a full-fledged picnic lunch. We were told not to stray too far from camp as we played with the kids.

We played hide-and-seek, and tag, and climbed the trees for a while, but I think we were all just going through the motions. It wasn't fun, and that constant worrying sensation in my stomach just wouldn't go away. It didn't help that the sound of mortar had not abated since that morning, and I had yet to see a single one land anywhere.

Sometime after lunch we heard helicopters overhead, and we all hailed.

"*Havanirooz!* The army's air force!" People started cheering. "Yay! Go kick some Iraqi butt!"

It took me a while to realize that the shelling had stopped. All through the day, like a nagging toothache, it had been in the background, and every time I'd thought it had stopped, there had been another bout.

Lunch, therefore, was fun, tasty, and enjoyable. We even laughed about the fact that we were in a forest during shelling.

"So now what's the philosophy behind that?" someone asked.

"I don't know." Dr. Kaveh shrugged. "The guard said this is the place to be during a war."

"He must have been thinking of ancient battles with swords and arrows."

Everyone laughed.

"Don't stray too far," Mom said, right after lunch, and we didn't. I yearned for the signal to pack and go back home and find Masoud and talk about all that had happened.

But…

Boom! Boom!

Darn! That sinking feeling again. Where are those darned helicopters to finish their job?

***

Everything happened pretty quickly from there. We packed and got in the car, and were whizzing out of the university and over the bridge.

"Where are we going?" I asked.

"Mollasani," Dad replied "That's forty miles north-east. It's safer there. We'll stay at Uncle Ghotb's."

Mollasani was a little satellite university housing complex next to the veterinary department where some of my dad's colleagues, including his best friend, Mr. Ghotb, lived. We used to visit there every once in a while. It was like the Kooy, but with much older buildings.

"We need gas," Dad said, but all the gas stations were shut down, and when we asked, they said that there had been a ban on all civilian gas sales and that they were saving the gas for the war effort. There was, of course, none of that being announced on the radio, which was playing military marches all the time.

"Duck kids," Mom said, urgently, and we went down.

We were used to the drill. Mom would give us the command when there was something going on outside that was not suitable for us to see.

"Oh my God!"

"What is it, Mom?" I asked.

"A missile has landed here," she said. "Please don't look… oh my God!"

We were going around a square on the edge of the city.

"Amir! Amir, we should help them." Mom's voice was anxious and tense.

I peeked out and saw a big group of people running next to our car, trying to hail it down.

"We don't have room," Dad said, as he slowed down.

"We have to help them."

We stopped and she pulled the window down. The crowd was in panic, incomprehensible, all talking at the same time. Sara, who had been sleeping in Mom's lap, woke up with a jump and started crying.

"What do you need?" Mom asked one of them, trying to soothe Sara at the same time.

"Just take my daughter to Ramin," the man said, out of breath.

"Ramin is on our way," Dad said. "Where's your daughter?"

"Right here, kind man, right here!" The man grabbed his daughter, who was holding a little boy's hand, and pushed them into the back seat next to Siamak. "They will go to her aunt's place. She knows her way. Thank you. Thank you, kind man."

It took us a while to get out of the crowd. People were stopping any car that went by.

"We have no room!" Mom kept shouting out her window.

When we were finally on the road out of the city, Mom turned to the girl. "What grade are you in, dear?"

"Third grade, Ma'am," she said politely, not smiling. She was wearing a light blue scarf, and was holding her quiet, wide-eyed, little brother tightly. The boy had shiny dark eyes and a runny nose.

"How old is your brother?"

"Three, Ma'am."

"You're a good girl, taking care of your little brother."

"Yes, Ma'am."

Mom turned back to stare at the road, and continued after a pause. "Don't you worry, little girl," she said. "Everything is going to be all right."

And I truly believed her.

"Everything is going to be all right." She repeated it, absent-mindedly, but somehow there was less conviction in her tone. I didn't like that and tried to ignore it, staring outside, trying to decide if that was smoke out there in the horizon, or simply some far-away clouds. That's when Siamak nudged me softly and I turned to find that the little girl, looking out the other window, had a tear rolling down her cheek.

***

When we got to Mollasani, it was as if we were on one of our usual visits, except that we had to share the house with two other families, the Kavehs and the Mohebbis, and our parents were edgy and nervous all the time.

Everyone was trying hard to make it seem like everything was all right, but there were little things people did that gave away their state of stress and anxiety. Dr. Kaveh suddenly burst into loud declarations. Dr. Mohebbi had started a habit of twisting his hair around a finger and pulling it out. Mrs. Kaveh kept putting make-up on, four or five times a day, and Mrs. Mohebbi kept cooking food.

The first night was rather eventful. The power went out, just as in Ahwaz—maybe so the Iraqi planes would get lost—and we lit candles. Mom had placed one under a sofa so Sara would sleep in Uncle Ghotb's while we all had dinner at Dr. Shahidi's, next door. I went back to fetch something when I noticed a blanket of smoke on the ground. I quickly put the candle out and turned the sofa to find the underneath all burned out, but fortunately, there had been no flames. I opened the windows and ran back to call Mom.

Later that night, around one in the morning, I woke up to the sound of gunfire. It went on for quite a while. No one said anything; probably concentrating on wishing it to go away, but they surely couldn't have been sleeping with all this noise. It was clearly not celebratory, and it couldn't have been anti-aircraft—I could tell the difference between that and Kalashnikov machine gunfire by now—plus it was taking too long. I had some scary thoughts, like what if the Iraqis were here already? They could be closing in, around the block. Any minute now they'd burst into our house and start firing at anything that moved. I tried to keep very still.

**

The gunfire did finally die out, after what felt like an hour or so. We found out the next day that some leftist guerillas had decided to raid the local revolutionary guard headquarters half a mile down the road, but had been outgunned and fled the scene. I guess it's never a good time to take up arms against your country's government, but right at the start of a foreign enemy invasion is truly bad timing.

We spent the next few days playing a lot of soccer as our parents were deciding what to do. News from Ahwaz was not encouraging. Miraculously, the city had not fallen, perhaps due to the incompetence of the Iraqi army's tank units getting stuck in mud only a few miles out of town. But the shelling continued, and had even intensified at times. The gas pumps remained closed. Dad had a half-tank, which was far from enough to get us to Tehran and the relative safety of Maman Bahram's place, where the air raids were less frequent and there was no shelling.

Dad even contemplated topping the tank up with kerosene.

"Yeah, it'll take you to Tehran," the mechanic at the pump said.

"So, one-part kerosene for every two parts of gas, right?" Dad asked.

"Yeah." After a short pause, the mechanic added, "You'd have to buy a new engine in Tehran, though."

"What?"

"The soot will clog all the valves." His voice was cool and monotonic.

"It'll fuck up your engine."

So, of course, Dad decided against that.

Every night, the men would gather around outside, listening to foreign radios, waiting for any hopeful news. They'd place a radio set on the trunk of one of the parked cars, and half-listen, half-opine on the news of the day. One time, Dr. Kaveh spotted a fast-moving light amongst the stars in the night sky.

"Look!" he shouted. "Look!"

"Must be a satellite."

"Yes!" Dr. Kaveh was almost jumping with joy. "Of course, they would never leave us alone. The Americans are watching us. They won't let anyone harm us. This is nineteen eighty. They'll protect us."

Even at twelve I could see the absurdity of the situation, but I was quite surprised at how Dr. Kaveh's colleagues reacted with affirmative noises. Were they just being polite? Maybe there was some of that, but deep down, all these Western-educated professors wanted it to be true.

***

I think three days is some sort of an evolutionary limit on how long friends can tolerate living with each other, beyond which they start getting annoyed of each other's idiosyncrasies and find this sudden urge to 'go home.' Except that in our situation, in Mollasani, home was not an option. On the fourth day, everyone started packing for the nine-hour journey to Tehran. We probably cleared out the little that was left at the local grocery store. Somehow, though, all the food ended up in Dr. Mohebbi's car.

"Shouldn't we split the food?" Mom asked casually, not really taking the precaution that seriously herself.

"Oh, we've got everything packed already, it's too much work," Dr. Mohebbi said. "Anyway, we'll all be travelling together. Just honk if you need anything from my car."

As we set off, though, on the flat planes of Khuzestan, with the road stretching out in front of us and on to the horizon, Dr. Mohebbi's car kept getting smaller and smaller.

"Amir, try to keep up," Mom said.

"He's going pretty fast," Dad replied. "It's unsafe to go faster. Plus, I need to conserve gas until we get to a pump."

"How much do we have?"

Dad looked at the gauge. "Less than half. We'd be lucky if it gets us to Khorramabad."

By the time we got to the broken bridge, there was no Dr. Mohebbi in sight. We did catch up with Dr. Kaveh in his white Renault 5 though. The cars were in two lanes approaching the shallow part of the river.

"Remember, don't splash into it like last time," Dr. Kaveh called out to my dad.

Last time, coming back from summer vacations, our car had shut down in the middle of the river and we'd had to get pulled out by a bulldozer. The water was only a foot deep, but that's what happens when the spark plugs get wet.

"Have you seen the Mohebbis?" Mom called back.

"No. They must have crossed already. Maybe they're waiting on the other side."

We did cross the river without an incident this time, but Dr. Mohebbi's silver Toyota was nowhere to be seen. All the food was in Dr. Mohebbi's car, and we were hungry. There was no place to stop. Mom found a bag of dried-up French bread, and we had some water, so that was pretty much all we got for the next four hours of driving.

An hour or so later, we left the straight, flat roads of Khuzestan to enter the narrow, twisty roads through the majestic Zagros Mountains of Lorestan.

There was a very long line at the gas station outside of Pol-e-Dokhtar when we got there. The 'E' on the dashboard—and on our bellies— were blinking impatiently. After standing in the slow-moving line for a while, Mom, Sara, Sia, and I got out of the car to stretch and use the bathroom. We ran into several cars from our convoy waiting in line, but the Mohebbis were nowhere to be found.

"Oh, they didn't stop. They must be in Khorramabad by now," said Mrs. Sehat.

"Yeah, they had a full tank of gas." I could hear the disappointment in Mom's voice. "All the food is in their car."

After a brief, awkward pause with Mom staring at the horizon, Mrs. Sehat turned to us and, in her usual sweet voice, said, "Hi kids. Are you hungry? Care for a chicken sandwich?" Her voice was kinder than I'd ever heard it, and at that moment, I loved her almost as much as my own mother.

That was and has been, by far, the tastiest chicken sandwich I've ever eaten. It had just the right kind of chicken, just the right kind of pickles, just the right amount of mayo, just the right kind of bread, and, to top it all off, Mrs. Sehat was making the small bite-sized sandwiches on the spot and feeding us with her hands.

"Don't touch them, dears. Your hands may be dirty," she said with a warm smile.

We just couldn't get enough of it.

"Enough, kids, let's go. You've already eaten," Mom lied. "Thank you, Mrs. Sehat."

"That's their food and they may need it. We can't be eating other people's food, now can we?" Mom said, after we'd said goodbye to Mrs. Sehat and left their car.

We spent that afternoon playing guest and host with pretty much every car in the line that came from the Kooy. It was fun. One minute we'd be visiting with the Kavehs, the next minute, they'd be paying us back the visit at our car. The grown-ups were drinking tea and chatting, and we were running around with the kids, playing games.

One by one, the cars ahead of us filled up their tanks and bid us farewell. Only two or three cars left for us to get to the pump, the armed revolutionary guard started turning people away.

We drove up to the guard. "What's wrong sir?" Dad asked him.

"We're out of gas," he said, waving us on. "Please move on."

"But I'm out of gas!" Dad was panicking.

"Move on, sir," the guard repeated, more firmly. "Nothing I can do."

We parked the car in front of the station and Dad went to talk to the guard, but came back shortly.

"It's no use."

"What do we do now?" Mom asked. "We can't just wait here in the middle of nowhere. And it'll get dark in a couple of hours."

We were one of the last cars in line, and all our friends had either filled up their tanks and left, or already had enough gas to get them to Khorramabad, and so had left when the station shut down. No one had stayed behind for us. In these times the priorities were clear: get your own family to safety before worrying about others. We were alone and helpless standing next to that empty gas station, surrounded by imposing, treeless, rocky mountains.

"We'll have to find someone to tow us to the next gas station," Dad said as he started to cross the road. "You guys wait here."

Mom shook her head. "No. We'll stand next to you. That way it's more likely someone will stop."

So, we all stood around Dad as he tried to hail a car. Sara was fast asleep and after ten minutes or so of waiting, with every car whizzing by, I was thinking maybe if she woke up and started crying, we'd get more sympathy from people and someone would stop to help.

But help did finally arrive, in the shape of a big orange Mack dump truck that pulled over. Dad explained to the driver that he was a university professor fleeing the war in Ahwaz and that he needed help to get to the next gas station, or Khorramabad. The driver asked about the war and the situation in Ahwaz as he started tying a big rope to the front of our car.

"Shelling, huh?"

"Yeah," Dad replied. "Relentless shelling."

"Tsk-tsk. That's bad." The driver shook his head. Once the rope was secured, he said,

"OK. Let's go!"

"If I honk twice, that means something is wrong, OK?" said Dad.

"Sure." The driver smiled. "It's all good. Don't worry."

"Yeah, but just in case."

"Of course!" The happy-go-lucky driver shrugged.

We all got in. The truck honked a couple of times; Dad responded with a single honk, the truck accelerated, and the rope snapped. My dad honked twice, three times, four times, and the truck disappeared around the bend with the tow rope swerving behind it like a retreating snake.

Dad got out the car shouting, but of course if the guy didn't hear the honking, he was sure not to hear my dad, who, by now, was just simply cursing at everything.

"Goddamn it! Goddamn that rope! Goddamn that truck! Goddamn this useless car! Goddamn! Goddamn! Goddamn!"

Then another car pulled up. "What happened?" asked the curious driver. My dad explained the situation.

"I'll catch up with him," the guy said.

"It's an orange Mack truck with a rope dangling behind it," Dad called after the accelerating car. Then he added, mostly to himself, "You can't goddamn miss it."

Dad stood by the road trying to hail another truck, so we all got out of the car to stand beside him. Sara, now doing her part, woke up and started wailing her head off.

Dad turned to Mom. "You guys should hitch a ride to the city."

"What about you?"

"I'll try to get someone to tow the car," Dad said. "Worst case I'll sleep in the car tonight. They're bound to deliver gas to the station soon anyway."

Mom shook her head. "No."

"I'll be all right,"

"No," she repeated. "We're not leaving you alone."

Just at that moment, we heard a familiar honking sound from around the bend.

"He's come back!" I shouted, as the big orange truck appeared, with what seemed like a big bearish smile as its front bumper.

"The rope broke!" the driver said, laughing and stating the obvious.

My dad laughed back. "No kidding!"

He pulled over and stepped out and started conferring with Dad. I only heard snippets of what was being said, but I gathered the driver wanted to try towing again, and Dad thought it wouldn't work.

"Do you need to use the bathroom?" Mom asked me.

"No," I lied.

"Well, come anyway."

***

When we got back, the driver had a shovel in his hands and seemed to be forming the dirt and rocks from the side of the mountain into something. Dad was sweeping some rocks and dirt with his feet, but his attempts were more gestures of help than anything really useful.

"We're building a ramp," he said to us, with a schoolboy smile.

"A ramp?" Mom didn't look convinced.

"Yeah. We're going to load the car onto the truck!"

"You're crazy!" Mom said. "It won't fit!"

"It will! It will! We measured it. The size is just right."

"You're crazy," Mom said again, all the same.

When they were ready, Dad called, "OK, everybody get in!"

"Why don't you load the car first?" Mom asked, still skeptical.

"The doors won't open once we load the car," Dad said. "Unless you want to ride with the driver?"

"You mean we'll be trapped in there?"

"Just get in." Dad was getting tired and impatient.

It took Dad a few failed attempts and some reworking of the steep makeshift ramp to get the car over it, but they persevered and our '77 Nissan Datsun finally made it onto the back of the truck without a scratch. There were two inches of space on either side, but the back of the car was sticking out a few inches and the driver wasn't able to completely shut the gates. He tied it up with a chain and added the broken tow rope in for good measure.

"All good!" the driver called as he went to board the truck.

"Remember, two honks mean stop, OK?" Dad called back.

"Yeah, yeah."

We finally left the station, with the guard smiling at us as we rounded the bend.

We heard on the news, a few days later, that that very station had been bombarded by the Iraqis, and many folks waiting in line for gas had died. This was one of the first atrocities of the war that were brought to the attention of the international community, and that were duly ignored.

***

The hour-drive to Khorramabad was awesome. This was before SUVs and I'd never ridden this high above the road before. We rolled down the windows and sat in the sill, with one hand on the truck's side railing, whooping and laughing. Sara was pleasantly confused at the fact that she could actually sit in Dad's lap as he was 'driving,' and she kept honking the horn. We tried to stop her at first, but there was no reaction to the honking from the driver, so Dad started joking about it and even honked a 6/8 beat and started dancing in place.

It was dusk when we got to Khorramabad, and the truck found an elevated piece of land and backed into it. The driver got out and opened the truck gates, and after some more shovel work, signaled dad to back out.

We were dazed and exhausted from the trip, and pretty dirty. As we got out the car, quite a large crowd of Khorramabadis gathered around us asking questions about the state of the war and offering to help.

"Here's some milk for the baby."

"Please come to our humble house and be our guest."

"Do you need money?"

"Please let us know what you need. You are our guests."

These were ordinary people from a working-class neighborhood with little to share, but their radiant kindness to out-of-town strangers was overwhelming, and it brought my parents to tears.

A kind young lady in a chador was stroking my hair gently, and a couple of men were helping Dad get the truck gates locked up again. Someone handed Mom a glass of tea and a sugar cube, and Sara was holding a cotton doll with a black face and a big smile. We never found out who gave it to her.

The driver didn't accept any money and left. He was almost offended when my dad offered to pay him.

"Don't worry about it," he said, pushing my dad's hand back.

"But—"

"I said, don't worry about it." He looked more serious than we'd seen him all day.

We finally all got in the car and drove a few minutes up the hill to Khorramabad's Tourism Board Hotel.

Khorramabad is a beautiful ancient city in a valley completely surrounded by mountains. There's a huge ancient citadel on a hill in the center of town dating back to the Achaemenid Empire. The Tourism Board Hotel is on the southern foothills, overlooking the town. It was a decent hotel where we usually stayed the nights on our way to or from Tehran.

We were waiting in the lobby while Dad checked us in, restless to take a shower and go to bed, when Dad walked over from the reception desk and whispered something in Mom's ear.

Her face turned red with anger. "What?"

"Honey, it's just to get us in."

"No!"

"They have to do it," Dad explained. "This is a government-run hotel."

"I don't care." Mom was furious. "This is a free country. I'll go talk to them." And she went up to the reception desk.

I was too tired for this, whatever it was. Why couldn't we just do what they said and get the room?

Mom marched back, not having gotten her way.

"Mr. Babak!" she called to the doorman whom we knew from all the way back when we stayed at the hotel the first time, a few years before the revolution. He had a khaki military uniform on now, and no hat. Maybe he had joined the revolutionary guards or the Basij.

Mom pleaded her case for a few minutes but didn't get anywhere with him either. All the while, Mr. Babak had his head down, not looking at her, and answering her in a soft patronizing tone.

"OK, we're leaving then," she announced. "I mean, *really!*"

They had asked her to wear a hijab, she explained to us in the car, and she thought it demeaning and a blatant disregard for her human rights and freedom, and refused to do it as a matter of principle.

Quite frankly, at that moment, I didn't care for any of those matters and just wanted to go to bed. We ended up staying at the more modest Municipal Hotel that night. It was a few blocks downhill and we drove all the way there in neutral, to save gas. I was only half-awake and Siamak and Sara were fast asleep when we parked at the hotel.

***

The classroom was crowded. Very crowded. Boys only. The kids were rude. They were even rude to the teacher, making faces at him when he turned his head. I was all the way in the back, next to my neighbor. Not *my* neighbor, Grandma's neighbor. He was the only familiar face in the classroom, and maybe he was trying to be accommodating by showing me what kids got away with at Tehran schools, but it was intimidating, and I didn't like it. We weren't even facing the front of the class. The window was open and he was showing off his aerogami skills by tossing paper airplanes out on to the schoolyard pavement, trying to break his own record for distance.

When the recess bell went off, I realized that I hadn't heard a word of what the teacher had said. I didn't even know what subject he taught. I held tight to my binder and shuffled down the stairs feeling very anonymous.

In the schoolyard, I headed straight to the gate, and pushed it open. It wasn't locked and that didn't really surprise me. I cleared the corner and started to run as fast as I could, all the way home. Grandma's home.

Along the way, I ran into Siamak. At recess, he had fled his elementary school too, and so we both got home together, angry, dumping our stuff on the floor in protest, and sitting on the couch with arms folded.

"Is that the kids?" Dad called as he came downstairs.

"You're home early?" Mom looked surprised.

"Hrm!" We frowned.

"What's wrong?" they asked.

"I'm not going back!" I said.

"Neither am I!" Siamak added, a tear rolling down his cheek.

"But you know you can't quit school," said Dad.

"This is not my school." I ran upstairs to our room, also bursting into tears.

I couldn't remember the last time I had cried. I didn't like crying. It was for babies. Plus, it made your nose clog, and I hated that. But I couldn't help it. It just wouldn't stop. I cried so much that after a while I forgot what had started me crying in the first place, or maybe I was trying to distract myself to make it stop, so, as my crying went on, unabated, I thought about the Kooy, and the soccer tournament, and Lilly Shirzadeh playing defense while I guarded the goal, and our boasting that we were the best defensive team ever, impenetrable, like a wall, and I wondered if I loved her or just liked her as a friend, and I thought about the tadpoles I had left in a jar of water on my windowsill, and I thought about the KSS—the Kooy Secret Society—and our next play, and if we shouldn't ask Lilly if she'd like to play the alien's girlfriend, and of Masoud, and all the stories I had to remember to tell him when we met again...

But somehow, my crying wouldn't stop.

"Babak!"

It was Sia's excited voice from the other side of the door.

"Babak!" he called again. "I have good news. Open the door."

I wiped my face clean on the bedsheets and opened the door just a little. "What?"

"I made Mom promise we'd go back to Ahwaz the day the war is over!" he said, excitedly. "We can go to our own school!"

"Yeah?"

"She promised." He added, "Be happy, Babak, we're going home!"

***

Eight years later, as a student in a university in Tehran, upon hearing about Iran accepting the UN Resolution 598, and the imminent end of the war, the first thing that came to my mind, and echoed on for a few minutes, were those words: "Be happy, Babak, we're going home!"

How the meaning of that word had changed for me.

Home.

DOWNED FIGHTERS

*T*he war started for us with news of air raids against military facilities in Tehran. I was twelve and we were in Ahwaz at the time, the capital of the oil-rich province of Khuzestan, which was ironic, because nothing had changed there. Saddam started the war to annex Khuzestan, but everything was normal where we lived.

That all changed within a few days when the daily air raids on Ahwaz started and we got a first-hand taste of the war. Morning, noon, and evening, like clockwork, Iraqi Migs would fly in, make a lot of noise, miss their targets, and leave. A few minutes later, the air raid sirens would go off, always too late.

We fled Ahwaz as refugees and ended up at my grandparents' place in Tehran. New neighborhood, new friends, new school. It was all too much, and I wanted this bloody war to end as soon as possible and to go back home.

The general consensus was, indeed, that the era of countries invading their neighbors had long passed, and that 'the world' would never allow such a thing to happen. It was any day now before the UN, US, Europe, Russia... someone would knock some sense into this guy's head and civilization would prevail.

But it went on. Beyond a couple of weeks. Beyond a month or two. If it kept going like this, I'd have to start getting used to the idea of taking the first semester exams here in this strange new school!

It was around this time when a new ray of hope started shining on me. This was good! So good I decided not to share it with anyone so as not to ruin it.

The afternoon daily, *Ettela-at*, started publishing a table on its front page counting enemy losses. The table had two columns. In one they printed black silhouetted icons for the category—a soldier, a tank, a helicopter, a fighter jet—and the other column had the counts.

I started paying special attention to the values. It was hard to corroborate the counts for the first two columns, but the helicopter and fighter jet counts seemed to increment accurately. We used to buy the other major afternoon paper, *Kayhan*, as well as the morning papers, *Enghelab Eslami* and *Jomhuri Eslami*, and the reported downed fighters and choppers were more or less the same. My parents listened to the BBC and VOA on shortwave radio every day, but those stations seemed to grossly underreport the losses. Even in cases where the downed jet and the pilot were shown on TV, the foreign reports were very cautious, heavily qualifying everything and saying that the claims had not been verified by independent sources.

What made me so enthusiastically wait for *Ettela-at* to arrive every day after school, was the rate at which the fighters were being downed. Iraq, we all knew, had 300 Mig fighter jets. I plotted the counts published in the table and they seemed to be following a linear trajectory, and my estimate was that, within seven months, by the end of the schoolyear, Iraq would run out of fighter jets altogether.

Thinking back to it now, my naïveté was laughable. For a twelve-year-old, I should have known better, but I must have subconsciously blocked all rational thinking on this matter. I had lost hope in the politicians, the international institutions, the adults, the system. This was all that was left, and I refused to dilute my hope by sharing it with anyone or opening it to scrutiny, even by myself. This was a form of religious thinking. Faith, with strict blinders on.

I remember, at the beginning of the last semester, feeling secretly happy when the count, as I had predicted, got close to 250. *Saddam is running out of jets*, I was thinking. *The air raids will soon become less and less frequent, and he will have to come to the negotiating table.*

It was around that time that *Ettela-at* started becoming erratic in the way they published the table. First, the chart got relegated to the second or third page. Then, it went missing some days. I remember scouring through all the pages, including the ads, several times, in search of the table and not finding it.

The last time *Ettela-at* published the table, the big news of the day was the downing of three fighter jets above Isfahan, and the table was prominently displayed on the front page. Total jets downed: 292.

That was the day I lost hope in going back home to Ahwaz and accepted the fact that home was now someplace else.

It was hard. This seemed to have been the last shred of youthful optimism evaporating within me. Welcome to the dark, pessimistic reality of adulthood, where fantasies are simply lies we tell each other and our children, and no one believes in miracles. I flunked five courses at school that year and very nearly had to repeat eighth grade.

The air raids continued. Saddam bought French Mirages, 150 of them, and some Russian Mig 25s. When that didn't work, he started showering the cities with Scud missiles. Nobody was counting anymore, and I stopped reading the papers or listening to the news.

When the war did finally end, more than seven years later, I overheard the news in a taxicab heading home from college, and I was not happy. I was angry. Most people that day were angry. Nobody understood why it had to have gone on for so long. It is, I think, only when you still have hope in an outcome, that you are able to celebrate it. It is, otherwise, too late, and too painful.

TELEPHONE

*W*hen the Iran-Iraq War started, most of us left Ahwaz after a week or so of air raids and the day the shelling started. My best friend, Masoud, and his family stayed behind and only left a few months later when a major arms depot exploded over three intolerably loud days.

That's how, after eight years of living together on the university campus, we lost track of each other. All communication lines severed.

We stayed at my grandma's in Tehran, where I went to eighth grade, hating every minute of it. Much happened that year, and still, when I look back, I think of my thirteenth year as the worst year of my life. But nothing was more painful than missing my childhood friends.

Dad heard from colleagues that Masoud's family was in Rasht, but I had no way to contact him, and, in my new, strange context, his memory started to fade into something imaginary and unattainable.

When he finally called, I hardly recognized him. He sounded like a grown man.

"Babak!" came a deep voice on the line.

"Hello?" There was something vaguely familiar about the voice, but I couldn't quite recognize who this was.

"It's me, Masoud," he said, with a really soft 's,' as he always pronounced his name.

Somehow, I wasn't able to utter a word.

"Remember me?" he asked.

"Masoud, from Ahwaz?" By now I knew it was him, but I just couldn't believe it. It was as if someone was calling me from a past life.

They had moved to Tehran and he had called me as soon as he'd gotten his hands on a phone.

Oh, the joy! I was beyond myself. I couldn't wait to see him again.

***

We met at Laleh Park, near where I lived. I'd chuckled when he said he'd be carrying a Keyhan sports magazine so I could spot him, but he had truly changed. He was much taller than me, and he was even wearing a faint mustache!

"Are you a man yet?" he asked me discreetly, as soon as we got home.

"Of course," I lied, not quite sure what he meant.

Masoud's family had rented a place in a neighborhood which was a twenty-minute ride away from us. We would spend half a day together every few weeks, alternating between my grandma's and their place. My kid brother, Sia, and Masoud's younger brother, Kaivan, were good friends too, so it was a fun playdate for all of us. Masoud and I would spend half the time talking about 'grown-up' stuff and the other half comprised of some activity with the four of us—board games, G.I. Joes, indoor soccer with a couch pillow...

These visits though, needed to be coordinated. In those days, you didn't just drop in. We needed permission and a ride from our parents. To make things more complicated, we were sharing a phone with my grandma, and Masoud's home didn't even have one, so he had to use a payphone.

My mom didn't want us to meet every week because we needed to leave space for other events and activities, and, of course, homework and studying for various school exams. But every time a weekend came approaching when things seemed ready and in place for us to get together, the agony of waiting for Masoud to call began.

I would sprint to answer all phone calls, even though the protocol was that we'd wait for Grandma to answer first. But she didn't always hear the ring, and even when she did, there was a good chance the call would get disconnected when she started tapping on the receiver—signaling that the call was ours. A disconnected call meant a precious 2 rial coin being wasted for Masoud, and the chance he'd have to call back later when he had another coin. Even if he did, he'd have to go to the back of the line and wait his turn again. Payphones were pretty inconsistent already, and I really didn't want to put him through that ordeal, so I answered first, in spite of my mom's objections.

When he finally called, the sound of that coin fall, followed by his voice, was music to my ears.

"<click> Hello?" It sounded like he was talking from the bottom of a well.

"Oh, hi, Masoud. What's up?" I said, in a fake cool, matter-of-fact manner. As if I wasn't expecting him to call. As if I had many other important things to do, but, hey, I'll spend a few minutes on the phone with him, why not? Oh, the suppressed elation at the prospect of spending half a day back in that fantasy world of pre-war Ahwaz.

And then, Masoud stopped calling.

Weeks went by and there was no phone call. I had no way of reaching him and I felt desperate.

Sia was a pain in the butt, asking me every day why we weren't having a playdate, and I was running out of reasons why Masoud had gone silent. Surly he could find a 2 rial coin. Even if the payphone was broken he could call from the 1 toman phone at the local deli, as he sometimes did.

What if there was something wrong? Someone was sick, maybe. What if they had moved again?

I had an idea. I would send him a letter. I knew his street name but I wasn't sure of the address, so I took five pieces of paper, wrote a single word—'Telephone!'—on all of them, and posted them to all the street numbers I thought might be his.

Days went by. Nothing. The postal system being as unreliable and slow as it was back then, I wasn't expecting anything for at least a few days, but just as I was about to give up, two weeks after sending the letters, he finally called.

"<click> Hello?" came the familiar voice from the bottom of the well.

"MASOUD! Oh! Oh, hi, Masoud. What's up?" It was hard for me to contain my excitement, but I managed.

"My street number is 14."

"How many letters did you get?" I asked, with a chuckle.

"Two. The neighbor brought me one yesterday and I got one in the mail today," he replied. "How many did you send?"

"Five."

I never asked him why it had taken him so long to call. It wasn't important.

"So... wanna hang out this weekend?" he asked, making it sound like he didn't care.

Music to my ears.

THE SOCCER BOARD GAME

*I*n our early teens, my best friend, Masoud, and I, made a soccer-inspired board game that really took off beyond our imagination. It was shortly after the 1982 World Cup.

I'd followed soccer on and off before that, but the '82 World Cup was a turning point for me and many of my friends. It really opened our eyes to the beauty of the game and its peculiarities, many of which we found to resemble the peculiarities of life itself. Brazil was the hands-down best team of the tournament, playing the most exciting game, with every player an artist on the ball, and the teamwork a sort of improv-ballet. Yet they lost. They lost to the underdogs, Italy, whose game was ugly to watch and could be summarized as defend-your-goal-by-every-means-and-get-the-ball-to-Paolo-Rossi, who only got a handful of touches every game, but was sure to score most of them.

Being the romantic, wishy-washy kid that I was, I'd picked Italy to win it all at the end of the first round after they'd managed to qualify second from their group, only on goal difference over the third team. I also liked France, another underdog, with a game that was pretty—some said too pretty. Masoud picked Brazil and Germany. Siamak, my brother, who is three years younger than me, picked Argentina with the great Maradona, a soccer magician if there's ever been one—a one-man show of extraordinary talent and willpower. Masoud's brother, Kaivan, was four years younger than him. Kaivan picked England, ever the over-hyped team that never failed to disappoint.

I don't know if our picks reflected our own temperaments. It did both Masoud's and mine, I think. I've always been a come-from-behind kind of person, lurking in the shadows, trying to remain anonymous as long as I can, while contemplating my moves to fulfill an insatiable ambition.

Masoud is a perfectionist. He does have a romantic side, but he's also very much driven by science and logic. Kaivan and Sia? I don't know. They were the little brothers. We got first dibs and they simply picked from what was left.

In those years, soccer was only just making its way back into the media in Iran. After the revolution, soccer was frowned upon by the revolutionary government as a symbol of the west. Games stopped being telecast, at first to reduce the influence of decadent foreign cultures, and later on because they didn't have the money to pay for the TV rights.

By '82 the fervor was receding, but most games were not shown, or a summary was shown later in the day after all the female fans were censored out.

I listened to some of the games on my parents' shortwave radio, usually reserved for listening to the news in the hope that things would get better. But things had not gotten better, and the news was not as interesting to us anymore. Soccer was a good substitute. There was a referee, and teams generally abided by the rules of the game, and even if you lost, you always got another chance; the next tournament, maybe.

Masoud and I became friends when we were five. Our fathers were both entomology professors at Jondishapour University in Ahwaz, the capital of Iran's oil-rich southwestern province of Khuzestan. We lived on the university campus with friends that were mostly bilingual. Khuzestan was the target of Saddam's invasion when his army crossed the border in 1980. I'd lost track of Masoud for a year or so after the war began. We'd fled Ahwaz and were staying with my grandparents in Tehran, and Masoud's family went to Rasht, up north. By mid '81, they moved to Tehran and rented a place not too far from where we were. We'd started getting together on weekends once or twice a month.

Setting up the playdates was quite an ordeal. Masoud's family didn't have a phone. Their landlord lived downstairs and Masoud would occasionally use their phone to call me and set something up. I didn't have an easy way to reach him, and so sometimes, when I hadn't heard from him for a few weeks, I'd write him a letter, usually with a single word on it: "CALL!"

It was a forty-five-minute walk from our place, and we'd jump over a tall fence and run through a great big garbage strewn open field on our way there. To maximize our time with our friends, we'd usually run the whole way.

One time, I had run so fast I could hardly see Siamak trailing me from across the field. When he finally caught up to me, he told me about a strange man who had called him from the other side of the fence.

"He was red in the face, panting and sweating, and he had a big stick in his hand from between his legs that he was rubbing furiously, and he kept calling me in a soft voice to come and see his little monster," he said. "He must have been crazy or something."

Kaivan and Siamak were playing with Kaivan's G.I. Joes and Masoud and I were really bored that day when we came up with the new game. It was too hot to play outside. We'd talked a bit, but our friendship was really not about talking. It was about doing fun and cool things together.

Masoud's eyes widened suddenly. "Let's make up a new game!" he suggested, with a mischievous smile.

"What kind of game? Like a card game or something?"

"Yeah, something like that. What do you think?"

"I don't know," I said, adding, "It's not easy."

We thought about it for a while.

"How about a variation on backgammon?" I asked.

I wasn't really being very creative. I just remembered how my uncle Bahram and I had gotten bored of playing backgammon after a few hours at it, and how my uncle, who is eleven years older than me, suggested playing it a different way for a change. We played with a predetermined dice for a few games. Then we played with whatever dice we called, which was kind of boring. Then we played a game and wrote down all the dice we got and played it again with the same dice and the game ended up completely differently. We then switched sides and each of us played the other player's dice. It was fun and we learned a lot. Plus, it renewed the fun in going back to playing regular rules again, which we did for another hour or two thereafter.

So that's the kind of 'new game' I was thinking about, and I'd seen the edge I'd have over Masoud, having experienced the whole thing once before. (I forgot to say that our friendship was also very competitive.)

"No, no!" said Masoud. "Something brand new. You know, from scratch. Let's invent a new board game."

The challenge in his suggestion made me forget my disappointment in not doing the backgammon thing. Plus, I had a great idea.

"How about soccer?"

"A soccer board game? I like it..."

"Yeah, we'd have teams moving around on a playing board..."

"Like on a grid or something?"

"Yeah, we can do that."

"How would they score goals?" Masoud asked, half-knowing the answer already, but wanting my opinion.

"There's a ball, right? And the players have different abilities."

"Like... how?"

"You know, one player is good at shooting, another is better at dribbling the ball."

"We can have defensive players, playmakers, goalies ..."

"Yeah!"

We were having a lot of fun with the idea, energizing each other, almost reading each other's minds.

"We need some sort of lottery system for goalies to decide if a goal is scored or not. You know, like Monopoly," Masoud suggested.

"Yeah, so when someone takes a shot on goal, we pick a lottery card to see if he's scored or not."

Masoud made his voice funny and pretended to read a lottery card. "The ball has hit the post!"

"Or corner. Or goal-kick." I considered it for a moment. "We should make it hard to score goals. Just like real soccer. It should be a big deal, and some games should even be scoreless."

We both fell silent. We knew we had a great idea, and this was one of those moments when you're creating something and you think that you've got it all covered—that false feeling of having thought of the whole thing in one go. Details are really not important at that point. If you've solved the big problem, the finer detail should be a piece of cake.

Of course, it's never that easy, but that initial self-deception is really helpful and without it we'd never have actually started the project. Masoud found a large rectangular piece of glossy paper, about 150 cm by 50 cm, that he had probably bought for some school project. We drew horizontal and vertical lines on it with a big ruler and pencil until the whole thing was covered with boxes of 2 by 2 cm. We marked the center of the board as the kick-off spot and drew the half-way line and the penalty boxes, as well as the goal posts.

We then called Siamak and Kaivan, who reluctantly broke away from their pretend war game.

"Pick your team," Masoud told them.

"I don't want to be with Kaivan. You guys are too strong," Siamak started complaining.

"It's everyone for themselves. Pick a soccer team you want to own."

"Oh! I'm Brazil," Sia and Kaivan said, almost simultaneously.

"You can't be Brazil. I support Brazil. Didn't you support Argentina?"

"Yeah, OK, I'm Argentina," said Sia.

"I'm England," said Kaivan.

"OK, let's make our teams then," Masoud said, as he handed out pieces of white paper. "Cut out squares the size of the boxes on the grid here." He pointed at the soccer field that I was coloring light green with a crayon. "Write the name of your players on each piece."

Kaivan brought out a bunch of *Kayhan Varzeshi* weekly sports magazines out for use as reference and after ten minutes or so, we each had our team of players cut out, with names on them and colored accordingly: Masoud's Brazil was yellow and light blue. My Italy was all dark blue. Siamak's Argentina was light blue and white-striped, and Kaivan took a long time carefully drawing the Union Jack on each of his players, making it hard to read the player names, and got into a little bit of a fight over it with Masoud.

There was also an argument over what Kaivan would do during the first game, which was, of course, between Brazil and Italy. Siamak had already called being the referee, even though he didn't know any of the rules.

"You can be the linesman," I said.

"No! That's boring," Kaivan said.

"Why don't you just practice your team until it's your turn?" Masoud asked, in an annoyed voice.

"No!"

"Come on, Kaivan. Just watch the game and learn."

"No! That's not fair. At least let me be the referee in the second half."

"You can't change the referee half-way in the game!" Sia said.

"I know! You can be the commentator," I said.

He really liked that idea. In fact, it was so cool that Siamak wanted to be the commentator in the second half, but Kaivan wouldn't go for that. The moment we started placing our players on the board, we realized we were missing something.

"So, how do we move the players?" Sia asked.

Of course, we didn't let on that we had not thought of that.

"Each player has ten single moves and they have to spread it between their players," Masoud said.

"We should make it more random. Let's throw dice," I suggested.

"Yeah, we'll throw dice," Masoud declared. "And the total on the dice will be spread between the players for movement on the board."

"How do you pass or kick the ball?" Kaivan asked.

"You can use your dice to move the ball instead of the player."

"Cool!"

We flipped a coin, which Masoud won, and of course he wanted to switch sides and gave the starting ball to Italy. We were sitting comfortably and so, rather than getting up and changing places, we just rotated the field, which made us all laugh. Things were actually funnier that day—exciting and funny.

"Hey wait! We forgot the goalie lottery cards," Masoud said.

We made a deck of ten cards. Five of them described a goal in some detail, like 'The ball hit the horizontal bar, and bounced inside the line. You scored!' or 'The goalie touched the ball, but wasn't able to keep it out: GOAL!'

"This means half the shots on goal will be in. That's too high. Let's roll for the goal too," I said.

"But the goalie lottery cards are really cool," Siamak said, "we should use them."

"Well, how about if the goalie rolls a single die and if he doesn't reach the ball, then we pick a lottery card."

Everyone liked that idea.

"Let's have lottery cards in the field too. You know, so if someone lands on them, they can get injured, lose the ball, out of bounds…" I suggested.

"Great! Let's randomly mark the board with exclamation marks," Masoud said. He turned to Sia and Kaivin. "You guys make the in-game lottery cards."

We set out to work and made a new deck, placed a bunch of exclamation marks on the board, and were finally ready to play again, with Italy's Bruno Conti waiting for the whistle to kick things off.

Kaivan started the commentary.

"Good evening ladies and gentlemen, and welcome to the beautiful Bernabéu

Stadium, in the heart of Madrid, for the clash of the titans. Brazil is—"

"So how do you land on a lottery square?" Siamak interrupted.

We all fell silent.

Masoud was staring at the dice in his hands. I was still deciding on my formation. I liked how Masoud had placed his players, but I didn't want mine to mirror his. Plus, Italy was supposed to be a defensive team, but I couldn't figure out how to arrange my defense on the grid without two players ending up too close to one another.

Siamak was uncomfortable with the silence, or maybe just wanted to embarrass us to the point of acknowledging that we had indeed not thought of everything yet.

"So how do you land on a lottery square?" he asked again.

"Well, if you end up on a lottery square with the ball, then you have to pick the card," Masoud said, knowing that he was not quite answering the question.

"Why would you go on a lottery square voluntarily? Most of the cards are bad things." Sia wasn't taking it.

This was quite a downer compared to a few minutes ago. Was this all a stupid idea? I mean, if it were this simple, other people would surely have thought of it.

"Actually…" I was giving up on pretending we'd thought it all through. "How does the other team win the ball?" And as soon as I said it, I had a great idea.

"I know!"

"What?" Sia asked, impatiently.

I had to pause. I knew my idea was good and I wanted to enjoy every moment of it. I could see Masoud's brain working overtime as he looked at me with a smile. He was probably reviewing everything that was said in the last few minutes in search of a clue to my idea.

"We can throw dice to win the ball," I said triumphantly. "When a player with the ball ends up facing a player from the other team, they have to throw dice for the ball, and if the defender loses, he switches places with the other player."

"Yeah!" Masoud nodded approvingly. "That's great. It solves both problems."

"Wait," said Sia. "How does it solve—"

"Can't you see, you dumb nut? The defender can force the other player to end up on a lottery square." Oh, how I was enjoying this.

Sia thought about it some more, and finally said, "Oh!"

"Got it?"

"I got it." He was all smiles. "That's cool!"

"So, I'm sorry, how do you get the ball again?" Kaivan had not been listening, and this was a good thing, because it gave Siamak a chance to explain it to him, and use the word 'dumb nut' on him in the process, which made us all laugh again, relieved that the idea for the game was as good as we'd initially thought.

So, we got ready to play again.

"*Welcome, ladies and gentlemen, to the clash of the titans, Italy, the defensive-minded ugly winners—*"

"Hey!" I protested.

"Well they are," said Kaivan.

"Are you playing Conti up front? I thought he was a right wing," said Sia.

"I'm the coach. We are trying a new formation," I explained.

"What difference does it make? All the players are the same anyway," observed Kaivan, casually.

He was right. I'm not sure if he realized how right he was, but we all stopped to think it over as he carried on commentating.

"*It is a beautiful sunny day and we are at capacity here at the Bernabéu. The players are warming up in place and awaiting the referee's whistle to start the game. Zico's shirt is pretty untidy; did he forget to wash it after the last game?*"

Masoud picked the yellow color pencil and started touching up his player.

"You know, I think he's kinda right. The players shouldn't all be the same," Sia said, thoughtfully. "What's the difference between Zico and Junior then? Everyone knows Junior is an idiot and now he has an equal chance to score a goal. That's not right."

"Junior's not an idiot. Just because he laughs when he misses a chance doesn't mean he's an idiot," explained Masoud.

"That's right." Everyone looked at me, surprised.

"Not Masoud," I explained. "Junior's an idiot they put in their squad to add some comedy. I mean, Siamak's right."

"*There seems to be a delay in the game. It seems like the referee forgot to bring his whistle.*" Kaivan was commentating. The three of us were frozen in deep thought, though.

"Maybe we can add another lottery deck for the players?" Masoud suggested.

"We already have two decks," I said. "Plus, we'd need several decks, depending on the player."

"Yeah." Sia laughed. "We'd need a genius deck, a deck for ordinary players, and one for…?"

"…idiots!" We all laughed.

"No, that's stupid." I sounded more serious.

"How about we give each player a number value?" suggested Masoud. "And we add the player's number value to their dice for shots and moves."

"Yeah!"

There we were with another great idea. We all got excited about it and started debating the values we should use.

Masoud got a notebook and started writing down the rules. He started counting the squares in each half of the field and noticed that one half had one extra square in length. But it was OK. We made that part of the rules and decided it was a good thing: there's a slight advantage on taking one side over the other. We decided to play two halves of fifteen minutes, and to have the ref do the timekeeping. Each team was allotted a quota of player number values. In each team, you could only have one player with a player value of 5. Three 4s, five 3s, and the rest were 2s and 1s.

Masoud had the great idea of allowing each one of us to have more than one team. Our first team would have a stronger squad than our second team, and so on. We even decided to allow a number value of 1 for a goalie of our choice. We had a lot of fun picking our teams and ranking them.

We had at least one more false start on our first game before the initial set of rules were completed. It happened as soon as I kicked off the ball, starting to play my 6 and 4 dice. I decided to pass the ball from Conti to Tardelli, while moving Tardelli into space on the right side. I moved Tardelli straight up five spaces, and passed the ball diagonally from Conti.

"You can't do that!" protested Masoud.

"Why not?"

"You can't move the ball diagonally!"

"Who says so?" He wasn't being fair and I wasn't about to let him get away with it.

"It's in the rulebook." Masoud grinned as he finished writing it in the rulebook.

"Gimme that book." I jumped on him.

"*This is incredible. The coaches of the two teams are physically engaging each other and the game has hardly kicked off!"* Sia and Kaivan were loving it.

Siamak was frantically making a yellow and a red card while Masoud and I were in a friendly tussle match over the rulebook, and Kaivan had now switched to commentating a wrestling match.

"The Italian coach is an expert in Greco-Roman style and is going for the upper body as the Brazil coach is trying to release himself from the stranglehold..."

The field and the players got scattered all over the place and I finally got the rule book as Masoud was sitting on me pounding my shoulders. A remark from Kaivan made Masoud go for him and I decided to take Siamak who was red carding everyone. It was great!

That's around the time when Masoud's mom showed up with drinks and cookies. I'm not sure if she'd timed it or not, but it was the exact right thing at the exact right time.

After a cool-off and some delicious cookies, we started brainstorming the rules again.

"Seriously, I don't think moving the ball diagonally should be allowed," insisted Masoud.

"Don't start that again."

"OK, but not all players should be able to do it," Masoud compromised.

Sia nodded. "Yeah, some players are better at curving the ball."

We set about deciding how many players would have that ability per team. This opened a whole discussion about player special abilities. We decided to allow some players a bonus point when tackling a ball. Gentile in Italy, for instance, was a great defender, and if he got in an adjacent square to Eder who had the ball, we'd add one to his die against Eder's, increasing the chance that he'd win the ball from him.

"Is this game ever going to start?" complained Kaivan.

We never finished that game. Half-way in the first half, my dad showed up to pick us up and we had to leave.

***

Oh, how we were drunk with excitement the next few days. We couldn't contain ourselves. The first thing we did when we got home was to look for a big piece of glossy paper to draw our own soccer field. We spent hours making it look good. We knew most of the player names by heart, of course, but we paged through all our old sports magazines to find the player names for our teams that we were missing. We decided to each have a third team too, and I picked Poland. I only knew two of the players.

But we didn't play.

We decided that the game simply couldn't be played without the referee and commentator being present. It wasn't right to play without Masoud and Kaivan, anyway.

All week long I hoped upon hope that we'd have Masoud and Kaivan over on the weekend, but I knew it was a tall order. Mom would never let us spend two weekends in a row on playdates. There was always something: we had to visit with relatives, or I had to study for an exam, or, just plain and simple, having playdates every week was too much and we needed some peace and quiet.

I tried. I tried really hard. That week, I tried too hard as far as my mom was concerned, and ended up being disrespectful of her by raising my voice. I was trying to explain the game to her, and how ground-breaking and important it had been for us to invent it. But she wouldn't listen. I knew I'd compromise the whole thing if I lost my temper, but I lost it anyway. I don't think I was being irrational. It's just that I had realized she would simply not change her mind, and so I might as well explode on her to relieve myself.

Well, that was a bad call. We got grounded for two weeks.

***

Of course, by the second weekend, things had calmed down and I tried my best to get Mom to change her mind, but she had a great memory for punishments and she had not forgotten. I didn't have the stomach to start another big fight with her and get the silent treatment for three days.

The silent treatment was the worst punishment of all. I hated it. She'd practically ignore me for two or three days, and, save for terse single-word communications, all I got was a frown. In my teenage mind, I interpreted it as hatred. How else could you sustain anger for that long? The whole thing would end with a speech from her, and a solemn promise from me, after which I'd get the warm smile I'd been craving, seemingly forever.

Getting together with Masoud was therefore out of the question for that Friday, and we didn't have much else to do, and when my Uncle Siamak offered to take me to his work, I shrugged and went along.

***

My Uncle Siamak was a communist. He was the ideologue of a group that called itself the Iranian Communists Union. He was quite a character. I really didn't know him much before the revolution when he was a student in the US, but he returned shortly before the Shah was toppled, and stayed at my grandparents' place during the year or two after the war started. That's when we had also fled Ahwaz to stay with them. He'd lock himself up in his room upstairs, smoking and reading through the night, and writing. I didn't know much about what he was up to, and quite frankly, I wasn't much of a revolutionary myself.

So, when I got into his car that day, it was almost like going for a ride with a distant acquaintance you hardly know. I think he had a similar feeling towards me.

"Now you'll know what I'm up to," he said, with a smile.

I smiled back, nodding.

"We're going to where the weekly is prepared for publication."

"Are you the boss?" I asked.

"There are no bosses. In our system everyone plays a role," he replied. "That's how it should be."

I was starting to think that this might not be as interesting as I'd hoped. Plus, I couldn't quite understand why we weren't taking my brother Siamak along. Just as we turned the corner, I spotted my older uncle's car, packed with his whole family, turning towards our house. He noticed us and honked his horn, and Uncle Siamak stopped.

My Uncle Kourosh was an Americanized capitalist, with strong patriotic views on Iran. He was a member of the National Front. I don't know if he got along with his brother or not. I think there was a big age difference between them. I don't remember them ever discussing politics, and they seemed to be quite nice to one another in family gatherings.

"Babak! Where are you going? We came to pick you up," Teri, my uncle's American wife, called out.

I looked at her inquisitively, not knowing what to say.

"They're showing a Charlie Brown movie at the Hyatt. Wanna go?" she asked.

I looked at Uncle Siamak.

He chuckled. "You can go, if you want."

I hesitated.

"That's OK. We can do this some other time."

I dashed out, not looking back.

Of course, that 'other time' never came. Shortly thereafter, there was a big crackdown on leftists, and they shut down my uncle's weekly. He disappeared a few days later, without saying goodbye.

***

We did finally get together again the following week when Masoud and Kaivan came over to our place. We played our first full games on our field, and it was a blast. Due to some obvious time-killing tactics, we decided to use a stopwatch and to stop the clock at the referee's discretion, so the games took around two hours each.

The commentary was also funny, because the moves were much slower than real-time and so a dangerous situation that would normally take a few seconds in real soccer, would take five to ten minutes here, during which the commentator had to sustain his excitement.

"Maradona with the ball... He's in a great position to shoot... in front of the goal... with the ball... Looks at Dasayev... Dasayev looks back... [Come on already! Roll that dice!] *Such a dangerous situation here... Will Maradona take the shot? Or is he going to pass? Dasayev looks ready... Maradona with the ball... This is dangerous... It's Maradona... With the ball..."*

We also had moments of confusion because of gaping holes in the rules. The ref would ask me or Masoud, and inevitably, we'd make something up, and Masoud would write it down in his little FIFA rulebook.

"I wanna sub!"

"You can't put your player there!"

"Why not?"

"You should have him run in from the side."

"What? That'll take forever."

"What do we do, Masoud?"

"Um... easy... just place the new player in place of the guy you're subbing out." And he'd start scribbling in his book.

After the second game, we spent a lot of time talking about the games.

"Did you see that pass Passarella gave to Ardiles on the right?"

"Yeah, Ardiles was lucky there weren't any players there."

We were careful not to talk about the dice or the person moving the players. It made it more real to imagine the whole thing actually happened.

"We should start a World Cup," Masoud announced, suddenly.

"Yeah!"

"If we pick one more team each, we'd be able to do four groups of four teams each," I said.

"We can do a draw and have one of our teams in each group. We'd have to make sure each group has one first team, one second, one third, and one fourth."

I was already getting a piece of paper and everyone was thinking about their choice of a fourth team. Russia, Algeria, Ireland, … Iran! Oh right, Iran. We'd completely forgotten about that. Of course, we all totally supported Iran, but the last time they'd made it to the World Cup was in 1978, before the revolution, and by now that seemed like ages ago. We didn't even have a national league. Even so, owning Iran as a fourth team was a great idea, and I was proud of myself for being so creative.

That night, Siamak and I were so excited, we started a magazine. We can probably boast that we started the first magazine in Iran that was exclusively dedicated to soccer. We called it 'Goal,' and it was complete with news items, interviews, a humor page, and even ads. We cut up all our real sports magazines to use the pictures and some of the stock headlines. We worked on it well into the night, deciding to keep it a secret until the next time we met our friends. The magazine's introduction to the world would coincide with the kick-off of our World Cup.

***

During those same days, the leftists, having found themselves completely taken out of the political game, were waging a war against the Islamic regime. By 1982, most of them had been rooted out, but every once in a while, a group of them, holed up in a repurposed house, would be discovered, there'd be a big shoot-out, and the government media would boast of having found and destroyed another 'team-house.'

When we went to Masoud's place for our World Cup openers, a 'team-house' had been discovered and destroyed in their neighborhood after a fierce and loud 12-hour gun fight the night before. It had kept Masoud and his family up all night, and he was enthusiastic to give us a tour. We followed him to the place, which was on the verge of crumbling.

"The revolutionary guards were behind this wall…" Masoud was the tour leader, even though I doubt that he'd gone inside yet himself. "… and the leftist guerrillas were on the second floor."

All the windows were shattered, and the door was broken. Everywhere we looked was riddled with bullet holes and we couldn't help but step on the shells and make a lot of noise as we entered.

There were traces of blood on the second floor, and a gaping hole where an RPG had exploded, marking the end of the gun battle as well as the guerillas. Just as we entered, someone from downstairs started shouting at us, ordering us to leave. It was probably a neighbor who had seen us sneak in and was worried that the building structure was too weak and dangerous.

**

As we silently walked towards Masoud's place, I couldn't help but think of Uncle Siamak. He had left home for a few weeks now and nobody seemed to know where he was. Was he living in a place like this, waiting to be discovered and slaughtered? I finally understood why my mom sounded so relieved a few days ago after finding out about my younger Uncle Bahram's situation.

Uncle Bahram had picked the wrong day to go see a movie—Chaplin's *The Great Dictator*. My mom had insisted on him not going that day. It was the very day the leftists had started their uprising against the regime and there had been gunfights on the streets of Tehran. A group of militias had hidden in the movie theater, and every young man walking out had been detained.

We'd not heard of Uncle Bahram for a month, during which my grandparents had searched up and down for him, and bribed, to no avail, anyone who seemed to be in a position of authority, or who claimed to know someone who was, to get some information.

"At least now we know where Bahram is," Mom had said, sounding relieved, once we were told that Uncle Bahram was held at Evin Prison, awaiting trial.

**

The moment we got to Masoud's house, all was forgotten. Masoud and Kaivan had pulled the chairs back and set the soccer field up on their dining table, complete with a scoreboard, and spectator stands full of people sitting all around the field. It was great.

"We couldn't sleep last night, so we did all this," Masoud said, proudly.

So, without missing a moment, we set out to start the World Cup, getting the teams ready for our kick-off match.

"I have an announcement to make," I said, taking the magazine out of my backpack. "I hereby introduce to the world, the first issue of…" I held the magazine over my head, turning slowly so all the spectators could see. "Goal Magazine!"

Masoud and Kaivan were gaping with awe.

"Wow! Let me see it." Masoud snatched it out of my hand and started reading. "Cool!"

The four of us leaned over the magazine. It was a very proud moment for Sia and me.

"We will publish one too," Masoud announced, looking at Kaivan and nodding his head. "We will have rival publications!"

"Cool," I said, savoring the thought of it.

"By the way, guys, we need to interview the coaches before the game," said Siamak.

It was fun. We even interviewed some of the players. We did fight a little over who'd do the interview, but we settled on taking turns. One would ask the questions, the other would take notes. Siamak and I would interview Kaivan and Masoud's teams, and they'd interview ours. We were dead serious, but, of course, we couldn't keep our team prejudices out of it entirely.

"Well, we have an attacking posture in our game today and we hope to win all two points," Cesar Menotti, the Argentine coach, was saying.

"Are you going to resort to any of your usual anti-football tactics in this game?" the reporter (Masoud) asked.

"What do you mean? We never sink as low as the Brazilians," Menotti replied with a frown.

"Oh, but the Brazilians are famous for a clean and beautiful game. The Argentines, on the other hand, do have an attitude of win-at-any-expense now, don't they?" the reporter retorted.

"Who is this guy?" Menotti demanded. "Can I get a *real* journalist?"

"Menotti exploded at the reporters before the game. It seems like the pressures of the competition are getting to him," Masoud said, as he pretended to be jotting it all down in his notebook.

The opener, between Argentina and Spain, finished 2-1 for Argentina, which was OK for both sides, because Masoud didn't expect much of his third team anyway.

"What happens if two teams that belong to the same person get drawn to play each other?" Siamak asked.

"Well…" I thought about it for a moment. "You can just call the result."

"Yeah," Masoud confirmed. "No need for us all to sit around watching you play yourself."

We played four games that day. It took us the whole day and we hardly had time for anything else. We even brought our lunch to the stadium. Lunch at Masoud's was always fabulously tasty. To die for. Masoud's mom was a genius in the kitchen. But this was the World Cup! I don't remember what we had for lunch that day.

***

The next weekend we were banned from a playdate, because we'd "only just had one last week," according to my mom.

On the Thursday, Uncle Kourosh took Siamak and me to his office. Having studied and lived in the US for years, Uncle Kourosh was quite the entrepreneur. At that time, he was the CEO of two companies. One, I think, was a construction company, I'm not sure. In fact, I'm not sure what my uncle did at his companies. It seemed like they had a different project every time I went there. They kept talking about a huge construction project for the government in the south, but then, I remember, there was a room at the office packed with some sort of toy owl they were distributing. They gave me one and I faked a lot of enthusiasm for it, but it was pretty boring.

My uncle was clearly the boss. From the moment we got there he'd be in his big office, smoking a cigar and on the phone, or in meetings. So that day they planted us in the meeting room and pretty much abandoned us for the rest of the day. We had plenty to do, though. We had a magazine to publish, so we set out to work, writing the articles and cutting out the pictures.

"What are you boys working on? Is this your homework?" Some

important guy at the office had just wandered into the room and, as was usually the case, was trying to endear himself to us in a very patronizing way.

"We're working on a soccer magazine," I said.

"Wow!" He noticed the cut-up sports magazines. "This is great! You're writing your own soccer magazine, are you? I love soccer!" He thought for a second. "Maybe I can help you…" He dashed out.

Sia and I looked at each other wondering what he was up to. The next moment, he burst back into the room with a file full of light blue transparent sheets with black letters of different fonts on them.

"This is Letrafix," he said. "You place the sheet on the paper where you want the letter, and you rub the back." He showed us. "And the letter will peel off onto the paper!"

"Wow!" This was wonderful. We could actually print authentic headlines with this stuff.

He left the file with us and hurried out to a meeting. We worked on the magazine for another three hours, and it was mostly done before he was back.

"Look at that!" he marveled. "Looks professional."

He picked the issue up and started flipping through it, but the more he read, the more his face grew confused.

"Algeria drew with France?" he asked, genuinely surprised. "When was this? Is there a World Cup on again already? When did Spain play Argentina?"

"Um…" I started explaining.

"Isn't Jim Leighton Scottish? That's Alan Rough, isn't it?" He was pointing at the picture of the Irish goalie I had discovered and called to the Irish national team. He'd done so well in his first game. The problem was, I didn't know his nationality and I just used a random goalie picture.

"Um, this isn't real," I said.

"It's not?" He couldn't hide his disappointment.

"I mean, it's not real soccer." I was trying to be helpful but I knew he'd never understand. "It's a game we invented."

"A game you invented," he repeated, absentmindedly. He set the magazine down, looking at us, kind of strange. "Good luck," he said, quickly, and left the room.

***

It took us four or five months to finish that first World Cup, and France, my second team, won it, after beating Masoud's Brazil in the final. It was as if we'd just lived an alternative reality to the actual World Cup of the previous year in which a deserving France had fought hard, but lost to Brazil's skills and experience in the second round.

We'd improved our tactical skills and formation choices with each game, and the last few games took a lot of brainpower and time. Not all games had been about skills though. In fact, luck had an important and sometimes overwhelming role to play, as I suspect it does in real life soccer as well.

There was one game in particular that stood out and has been talked about ever since: Italy versus Algeria in the first round. Italy, of course, was my first team, and so had my best players. Algeria was Kaivan's fourth team. They didn't even have a five-shooter (adds five to the die and allows diagonal shots). Most of the players were three's and two's, and there were only two weak dribblers on the team. Ordinarily, this would have been an easy win, as had been the case in all other games between a top and third or fourth team. But this time, things went very badly for Italy, right from the start.

At kick-off, Mustafa Dahleb, the Algerian striker, ran the ball down the field with none of the Italian players reaching him. This was despite the defensive formation, with five defenders, and three mid-fielders helping on defense. Dahleb took a shot from well outside the box, out of reach of the goalie. The ball hit both vertical posts and went in! Kaivan was very happy and danced and taunted me for a while, so much so that the referee (Siamak) had to threaten him with a yellow card if he didn't get back to the game. I laughed along with him. It was indeed a spectacular goal, but surely Italy would easily be able to get back into the game.

But it wasn't to be. After a few passes, Algeria won the ball and pushed it forward. This time Gentile, the superstar Italian defender, was there to try to stop him. Gentile was an excellent dribbler. Two points would be added to a roll of dice for him when hustling for the ball. The player in front of him was Dahleb. Not only was he able to dribble past Gentile, who had stationed himself on a lottery square, according to the card that got drawn, Gentile injured himself badly and had to be subbed out for a lesser defender. Dahleb went on to score that goal too.

The first half finished at 2-nil, and the Algerian defense and goal held up to the relentless attacks of Italy. During the break, Kaivan and

Siamak would not stop making fun of Italy. Worst of all was the one-sided commentary of Masoud.

"This, ladies and gentlemen, is an incredible display of fine soccer from Algeria. We should, of course, also mention how poorly the Italians have been playing. Too much pride, perhaps? Or too much partying last night? Who knows? I suspect the main problem is not the players, but the coach…"

"Shut up!"

"You can clearly read the frustration on the face of Cesar Menotti, the Italian coach. I hope he doesn't have a heart attack…"

I smiled at that and tried to keep my cool. At least, I thought, Algeria had been so lucky in the first half that, sooner or later, their luck would surely run out, and that's when they'd get trampled.

It wasn't to be. As soon as the Italian players kicked the ball off, Bruno Conti was red-carded after punching an Algerian defender. The ball was then passed to Mustafa Dahleb, who took it all the way to the Italian goal, won a penalty, and converted it.

This was unreal! I couldn't believe it. No one could be this lucky. It should be illegal.

"Argh!" I cried, and ran to the wooden closet on the side of the room and punched it with all my might. The gang, who had remained quiet, looking on as I was having my fit of rage, suddenly burst into laughter. That's when I noticed that my fist had actually broken a hole into the closet door and my hand was inside the closet. I was totally surprised and laughing myself now. I carefully pulled my hand out so as not to bruise it on the broken wood, which was actually much thinner than I'd expected. As I got back to the game, there was another burst of laughter as Siamak calmly drew the yellow card out of his pocket and held it up to me, adding insult to my injury.

Italy lost that game by the amazing score of five to three and was eliminated from the games, as was Algeria, who lost its remaining two games and was out, too. But the legend of Mustafa Dahleb lives on, and to this day, more than thirty years later, the story is still told and retold, every time the four of us meet.

***

After the World Cup we stopped playing for a month or two, but most of our energy was still focused on the game. Special editions of 'Goal' and

'The World of Soccer' were published, with centerfolds and extra pages.

We also spent time organizing a club championship tournament. Each of us picked a few clubs and started the rosters off of the real club rosters we found in the sports magazines. But then the whole fun was in trading players. There was a restriction of three foreign players per club. We also allowed up to two additional players to transfer in between clubs each of us owned, as inside transfers and loans. The kick-off was scheduled for our next get together, in early July, when it was suddenly delayed due to unforeseen events.

It was a Saturday, visitation day for my Uncle Bahram, when my mom came home laughing. It was a kind of nervous laughter, but it seemed quite real.

"He's there too!" she was saying. Uncle Kourosh had been detained a few weeks before and was serving a nine-month sentence, but that we knew, so who was she talking about?

"Siamak?" My grandma guessed it.

Mom nodded her head slightly to invite my grandma to laugh along with her, for obviously it was very funny.

I was up the stairs watching through the railing when Siamak came out of the room. "What's going on?" he whispered.

"Uncle Siamak is in prison." I wasn't sure.

"Why's that funny?"

I shrugged. We looked on for a while. My dad came in too, having parked the car, and he had a great big smile on his face. Then came my grandpa. When he got the news, he let out a deep sigh and said, "Thank God!"

My mom eventually spotted us up the stairs and noticed the concerned and inquiring look on our faces.

"Why are you guys worried?" she asked.

"Why are you all laughing?" I asked hesitantly, feeling somewhat stupid for not knowing.

"Oh! Well, at the end of our visitation with Uncle Bahram," Mom explained, "we went to check to see if your Uncle Kourosh is allowed visitations yet." She hesitated, building up to the punch line. "And guess whose name we ran into on the board?"

"Uncle Siamak?"

"Yes!" Her face was genuinely happy. "He's there. All three of them are at Hotel Evin!"

"Why is that a good thing?" I asked, feeling quite worried now.

"My little darlings, can't you see?" She sat down beside us, hugging us both with each arm. "This means your Uncle Siamak is alive. We've been very worried about them, and now we know where they all are."

I think I managed a forced smile in response.

"Soon they will find out that none of them have done anything wrong and they will all come home," She said, though unconvincingly.

That was a scary experience for me and, I'm sure, for Siamak too. Watching your parents do what mine did that day can really rattle you. Up until then, I'd always thought of my parents as dependable pillars of rationality, but now, no matter how I looked at the whole thing, it made no sense whatsoever. *Has the trauma of the recent times driven them insane? Is this what people do when they go crazy? Can I rely on them to make the right decisions for us going forward? That's too much responsibility! I'm only thirteen, goddamn it!*

These thoughts kept going through my head over and over again, and I hated it. I preferred not to think at all, for a while. I'd heard that it was not possible: not to think. But I tried. I just sat in my room staring at a random point on the paper soccer field and playing with a piece of lint on the carpet.

I don't know how long I spent there thinking about not thinking, but it must have been a while. The incident had happened in the early afternoon, and I suddenly realized that Grandma was calling us down to dinner and it was dark outside. I didn't listen much to what was said at dinner and went to bed right after. Mom came up a little later and kissed me good night.

"Are you OK?" she asked.

"Yeah."

"You're in bed early. Are you feeling sick?"

"No."

"Is anything wrong?"

"No. I'm just tired," I lied, trying with all my might to suppress the butterflies that had been flying around in my stomach since that afternoon.

"You're not worried about anything, are you?"

"No."

She kissed me again, and her kiss did help a lot with the constant sinking feeling. But I lay awake, I don't know how long, still trying to not think about anything. It wasn't that hard, but it wasn't helping much with the worry, either.

Later that night I heard Mom and Dad whispering for a long time in their room next door. I knew what that meant. They made big decisions that way and they must have been making one right then.

The next morning at breakfast I thought Mom looked like she had an important announcement to make, and I was right. The moment we all took our seats she told us that she and Dad had decided that we all needed a break from the stress of the last few months, and that we'd be leaving for Shomal the next morning and we'd stay there for a while.

My parents and grandparents, along with Uncle Kourosh, had bought a little cabin by the Caspian Sea up north, or Shomal, in Farsi. We used to love going there for a few weeks every summer. I thought this was a great idea, and good timing too, right after the World Cup. The first thing I did after breakfast was to write a short letter to Masoud:

We're leaving for Shomal tomorrow. The club championship games are hereby postponed by a few weeks.

***

As it turned out, we stayed up north all of summer that year. It was hot and very humid. The seaside was nice, although Mom couldn't come along with us any more due to the new government restrictions— women had their own barricaded swimming areas now—but Dad would take us to the men's swimming area every once in a while. We played backgammon and cards at home, read a lot of books, and invented a kind of squash-like game off the wall in the yard with Siamak that was fun, but most of our time, we spent with Bijan and our local friends.

Bijan was the son of the owner of the greenhouse and plant store next door. Shomal, being the humid lush green place that it was, inspired many vacationers to buy plants on their way home to Tehran, where the plants would inevitably die in the dry weather, so business was good for Bijan and his family. I used to hang out with him when we were up north, and I made good friends with a lot of the local kids through him.

His dad didn't like him to be distracted from work so, when he was at the store, Bijan was busy, and we'd know to stay away. But they had two stores and his dad worked at a botanical garden on the other side of town too. When Bijan turned on the light in the corner of the greenhouse, that was our signal that the coast was clear and we'd climb on to the wall next to our porch and walk over to the plant store's large backyard and jump in to go play with him in the greenhouse.

"Hey!"

"Hey."

"How's it going, City Boy?" We shook hands.

"Not too bad. How are you?"

"Doin' OK," Bijan said, as he cajoled a large pot of petunias into place.

We sat down and talked for a while, catching up on things. Bijan was an avid bookworm and we exchanged some book recommendations. We were reading a lot of Aziz Nesin those days. His books were full of funny short stories and sometimes, when we got bored, we'd read them out loud to one another. On that day, though, I was eager to get him up to speed on another important development.

"We invented a board game," I announced, trying to sound casual.

"A board game?"

"Yeah. Like Monopoly. But better." I could tell from his reaction that he wasn't particularly excited about Monopoly. "It's based on soccer."

I told him all about the game, how it was played, and the tournaments, and as I was speaking and he was watering the plants, moving the pots and clearing the dead leaves, he walked to the corner room where we weren't allowed to go and, after a few seconds, walked out with a big sheet of glossy paper. "Can we make one on this?" he asked me, grinning,

"Of course!" I was really happy that he was interested. "We need a ruler and a pen to draw the squares. Sia, go grab some colored pencils."

Siamak ran off, without complaining about me being bossy or why he should do all the hard work. This was big!

That summer, we taught all the Shomal gang how to play board soccer. Of course, Siamak and I had our same top two teams, but the other teams were divvied up between the kids, and we started a tournament. I enjoyed being the sole mitigator of disputes and the only reference on FIFA rules in the absence of Masoud. Siamak was there to keep me honest but it was easier to deal with him, and he played along. We played one or two games a day that summer and by the time we were ready to leave for Tehran, the game had found a life of its own out there, with three boards having been made and home and away games being played between the bakery, the dairy market, and the plant store stadiums. To avoid interruptions, we assigned two players per team so one could carry on with the game while the other attended to customers, phone calls, or parents dropping in.

***

Back at our place in Tehran, I told Masoud all about the Shomali kids' enthusiasm for the game.

"You know, if we publish and sell this game, we'd make a ton of money." His eyes lit up with the idea.

"I know," I said, even though I had not thought of that.

"We should patent it."

"Yeah." We both fell silent thinking about it.

"How do you patent something?" I finally asked.

"I don't know," Masoud admitted. "We should ask around."

"You know, there's a place on the main street near here that sells Iropoly." This was an Iranian knock off of Monopoly. "We should go ask them." After a brief silence, I asked, "Wanna go now?"

"Sure!" Masoud said without missing a beat.

Tehran didn't have that many boutique stores back then. In fact, they had become so rare that any store selling non-vital bootleg foreign items was called a boutique. This was mainly stuff smuggled into the country by the few travelers coming from abroad. It was typical to walk into a boutique and find a few books next to an assortment of fancy shirts, next to cans of soda or chocolate bars.

Amir Abad, the main street near my grandparents' place, had two such boutiques. We'd occasionally wander into them to see if they had anything new. It was sort of like visiting a museum, a reminder of a distant era. In one such place, I'd once spotted a few boxes of breakfast cereal with expired sell-by dates. I had immediately run out to fetch Siamak.

"Look at that! They've got Honey Smacks!"

"Cool!"

We both knew buying a box was out of the question. We didn't mind the expiration date. It was the crazy high price that was prohibitive. We had a pretty good substitute for cereal anyway: break dried lavash flatbread into a cup of milk and add some sugar. Mmm!

"There it is." I pointed at the blue Iropoly box on the top shelf of the store.

Masoud approached the counter. "Excuse me, may I see that?"

The owner looked suspiciously at us. "Do you want to buy?"

"We actually have a question about it," I said, politely. "I live in the neighborhood." It was important to show him that we were serious and didn't mean mischief.

"What is your question?" he asked as he reached for the box, hesitantly.

"Is it new?" Masoud asked.

"Of course it's new!" The owner said, half-offended. "I don't sell second-hand."

"Oh, we don't mean that," I explained. "We mean are they making Iropoly games again now."

"After the revolution," Masoud added.

"Oh, yes, this is new." The owner said placing the box in front of us and opening the lid. "Look. They've changed all the street names." He pointed at one called Mosadegh Avenue. "They can't keep up, though, can they?"

Mosadegh Avenue, the beautiful sycamore-lined street in Tehran stretches over fifteen miles from the Mountains up north, all the way to the main train station down south. It used to be called Pahlavi Street before the revolution, but, they changed it to Mosadegh, the popular prime minister of the '50s. Mosadegh, however, was not religious enough for some people in authority, and, only a few months ago, the name had changed again to Vali-Assr, the Shiite Messiah.

"May I?" Masoud asked, pointing at the contents of the box.

"Sure. Don't get it dirty or crumbled."

There was a little instruction leaflet with many typos and an almost unreadable font we looked through, but there was no mention of the publisher.

"Who makes it?" Masoud asked.

"I don't know. Why?"

"Well, we'd like to get in touch with the maker," I explained. "Who do you get it from?"

I don't think the shopkeeper liked that question much. It was probably an instinctive reaction from him.

"Some guy dropped them off the other day. I don't know him that well." He started packing the box again, carefully. "What's your business with the maker?"

"We..." I started explaining, but hesitated. I wasn't sure if he'd understand. "We have an idea for a game, and we thought maybe—"

"Maybe they'd give us some advice," Masoud said.

"Well!" The store owner smiled. "Well, well!" He sat down on his stool behind the counter again. "How old are you?"

"Thirteen."

"Good, good." His whole demeanor seemed calmer. "Where did you say you lived?" he asked me.

"Just over in Hey-at," I said. "Thank you very much, we need to go now." We sped out.

Those storekeepers could be a big waste of time. They were nosy and just looking for a way to pass time. We were probably the most exciting thing that had happened in that store for a while.

***

We played a lot of board soccer that year. Bayern Munich won the world club championships after beating Boca Juniors in extra time. England won the Euros. More than twenty issues of Goal and The World of Soccer were published and the journalistic rivalry seemed to be helping the sales. We spent all our time together playing the game, and the rest, obsessing over the magazines.

It helped us through some rough times at home, the execution of Uncle Siamak being the worst. Thinking back, our parents may have appreciated the fact that we were distracted by it, and getting permission from them to go to Masoud's seemed to be easier during that time.

But all good things must come to an end, and the end of the game for us came rather abruptly, as most decisions from my mom tended to be executed. It was towards the end of my tenth grade and the Konkoor was upon me in two short years. There was a war going on and, in those years, if you didn't pass the university entrance exam, the Konkoor, you were drafted to fight at the front against Iraq. So, to us it was a matter of life and death. Many of my well-off friends didn't take that risk and their parents sent them abroad before the cut-off age of fifteen when they were banned by law from leaving the country until they'd served. Our class at the high school in ninth grade shrank from 40 kids to 25 by the time the school year ended. By tenth grade, though, we were stuck. It was study or die.

My mom secretly talked to Masoud's mom and they decided they should cut down on our visits and ban the soccer board game in order to keep us focused on our studies for the Konkoor, and one day, when we got home from school, Mom had gone through all our stuff and had gotten rid of the game board, all the teams, and all the magazines.

When she sat us down to announce it, I knew she had some important message, but backing it up with such drastic measures underscored the importance.

"Today I went through your things and got rid of anything that might distract you from your studies," she said, looking us in the eye. "I know it is hard for you. I know you love your games and you've spent a lot of time on them. But that is exactly why you need my help. I am here to help you concentrate on your studies. Failing the Konkoor is not an option." She paused for effect again.

Facing Siamak, she continued. "Siamak, I know this is too early for you and Konkoor is still many years away, but I'm counting on your help with Babak. We all need to make sacrifices to pull through this." She faced me again. "Are you ready to make sacrifices?"

I nodded, wondering what she had in mind, but I was happy, deep down, that she was there, that she knew what she was doing, and that if I listened to her, everything would be all right.

"This is not like your eighth grade."

She had helped me through some rough times back then when I had flunked in five subjects, stunning the family.

"I can't help you with your math and physics; they are too advanced for me. The only help I can give you in your studies is to keep you from distractions and help you organize."

I knew the 'starting tomorrow' part of her speech was coming. I was impatient to hear what she had planned for me. How bad was it? Was there going to be any room for fun at all?

"Starting tomorrow, you will review ninth grade and practice taking tests as you finish each subject. You will study two hours in the morning and two hours in the afternoon. You will have your evenings to yourself. We will have to cut down on Friday plans because the four hours a day is in effect on holidays too."

She read the disappointment in my face.

"We need to start now, Babak. This is not a joke." Her face was stern. "You have two short years to prepare."

"OK." I nodded.

"If you stick to the plan, we will make sure we have one Friday a month for you and Siamak to do something fun, and perhaps even visit with your friends."

This was music to my ears. We would get to see Masoud and Kaivan every once in a while. My mom had a way of saying things that was very convincing.

***

And so that was the end of the game for us. Out of our control and abrupt, but I guess that's the only way to stop an addiction. The fact that Masoud and Kaivan had also been banned from playing made it a bit easier. We were all studying for the Konkoor and that was a big deal. Having been refugees of the war, we knew full well what was at stake.

Two years later, Masoud and I both got pretty good scores on our Konkoors and were accepted at good universities in Tehran. We'd all but forgotten about the game, and anyway, we couldn't revive it because Siamak and Kaivan were now busy studying for the dreaded exam.

I had stayed all the past two years in Tehran, but that summer, we spent a few days up north before the start of classes. It had been a while since I'd seen Bijan. I was quite worried for him. I knew he was a smart kid and that he wouldn't have a problem entering a top school if he set his mind to it, but he had the family business to take care of too. Would that give him enough time to study?

"Hey!" I spotted him sweeping the front of the store.

"Babak!"

We hugged.

"How's it going, buddy?" I didn't dare ask the question. "How's your dad? How's business?"

"I got into Sharif," he said, smiling proudly.

"You're kidding me!"

"I'm coming to Tehran!"

"Wow! This is unbelievable. I got into Sharif too! What's your major?"

"Mechanics."

"Mine's software."

We stood there, smiling. He was a quiet guy anyway, but I was at a loss for words. Bijan in Tehran was so out of context for me I simply couldn't imagine it.

"Come on in," Bijan said, finally. "I want to show you something."

As we entered the greenhouse, I could hear what sounded like a few kids arguing.

"Offside," one was saying.

"No," another said. "It's not offside if the ball's not passed to you yet."

"Is so."

"Dude! Read the rules."

A bunch of kids were huddled over a board with a soccer field drawn on it, square pieces of paper arranged on the board in an elaborate formation, and a paper representing the ball, sitting on one of them.

"You guys are still playing this?" I simply couldn't believe my eyes. I didn't even know these guys.

"It's the World Cup!" one of them explained. "Semifinals."

"Cool!" I exclaimed. "Who's playing?"

"Brazil-Iran."

"Iran?"

"Iran's pretty strong," the kid said, matter-of-factly.

"Bijan," one of the players started, "isn't Farshad Pious offside?"

"Let me see." Bijan leaned in, and I slipped into a nostalgic daydream.

***

Mom had pointed me to a drawer in which she'd stored some of my old papers, and I was sifting through stories I'd written through the years, picking out the ones I'd liked better, to take home with me, back to California. It was 2007. I was tired of reading *Harry Potter* to my nine-year-old every night, and figured he may appreciate something written by Daddy instead. That's when I ran into the old matchbox with the letters PSG written on it. It was my club team, Paris St. Germain. Somehow Mom had missed this one. Or maybe she'd kept it on purpose, as a tiny memento.

The players were still inside. I placed them on the carpet, one by one. Alan Giresse, four-shooter, Jean Tigana, three-shooter, Bernard Genghini, three-dribbler, Jean-Luc Ettori, goalie …

Six of them stood in the back, and five sat in front, smiling for one last team photo, with the entire stadium on their feet, cheering in remembrance of the good ol' days.

LONG-DISTANCE CALL

$\mathcal{W}$e had a few guests over to dinner and Dariush was late, as usual, probably taking one of his 'quick showers.' Dariush was my mom's cousin and everybody loved him. He was funny and charming, handsome and always well-groomed and smelling of aftershave. Every time he showed up, he brought an air of levity along with him, and our household smiled a little more when he was around.

Everything about him was cool, except for the fact that he suffered from a huge lack of self-esteem. Dariush was the family's perpetual match-making project. He never tired of seeking people's advice on marriage. At first, I used to listen intently to learn from the conversations, but after a while, the whole thing became repetitious and predictable. He also had a habit of never buying his own newspapers and always reading ours. I think he was stingy, but at the time, being fifteen, I didn't know that. I just loved him for his character.

When he finally arrived, he was in a rush to leave. "I've just come to get my quota of *Tah-dig* rice and go. I have a few phone calls to make."

"Where to?" Mom asked. "Why can't you make your phone calls from here?"

"Sudy-joon, these are international calls. They'd cost you a lot."

101

Dariush carefully picked the pieces of *Tah-dig* from the plate. "Of course, they won't cost me much," he added, half to himself.

"Really?" my dad, Amir, asked. "I didn't know you could do that in Iran."

"Do what?"

"You know, dial your way out of the country."

"What do you mean, Doctor?" Dariush was looking inquisitively through his thick glasses at my dad. "I thought there was only one way to dial out of the country."

"When Amir was a student in London, he learned of a way to dial internationally without having to pay international rates," Mom said. "Tell him the scheme, Amir."

"Oh, well, at that time if you knew the area code of adjacent regions, you could chain them together until you got to the area code local to your destination."

"Wow. That sounds hard."

"It was," Dad said, helping himself to another serving of chicken. "You had to know your geography and be good at dialing." He looked up with a smile. "It's not easy dialing a hundred numbers without making a mistake. And the dialing had a certain rhythm, and you had to wait after each area code was dialed to hear the click. There was a certain technique to it." He looked proud. "But it was dirt cheap, and once you finally succeeded, you just didn't want to hang up."

"Well, Doctor," Dariush said after a pause, "that is not how my phone call will end up being cheap."

"So, what's your technique?" Dad asked, but Dariush wasn't about to give it away that easily. He had a story to tell, and as usual, he had stolen everyone's attention.

"In fact," he said, ignoring my dad's question, "the phone call will be free."

"Of course," Mom joked, pointedly, "like making a call from our place would be free for you."

"No–no," Dariush said, playing into it, "not that kind of free."

After the laughing subsided, Dariush continued tickling our curiosity. "I need to run to make a free international phone call…"

"OK, already!" my grandma, Maman Bahram, jumped in impatiently. "Tell us the story."

"So, Uncle Ali called me right before I left home," he said. "He was driving home from work when he noticed a long line for one of the phone booths at the telephone center on Paasdaaraan. He asked the folks there what it was about, and they said the phone was broken and it was letting people make free calls."

"Really?" Maman Bahram was taking it very seriously now.

"Oh, yeah. That's where I'm headed. Anyone want to go?"

***

By the time Uncle Kourosh, Maman Bahram, and I drove up Paasdaaraan in Uncle Kourosh's Blazer, Dariush was around the halfway point in the long line, waiting to use the one broken phone out of the three booths on the curb.

I'm not sure why I went along. I was bored and this was an adventure. I felt grown-up and independent when Mom nodded her permission to go along. Of course, Sia was too little to go and my parents had to stay behind with him.

I missed my Uncle Kourosh's wife, Teri, and my cousins too. We had not heard from them for more than a year or so since they'd fled the country. They were in a free and peaceful side of the world. A world I had lived in, but that seemed remote and unreal to me now, almost three years after the revolution.

People took their time talking on the phone, but would go back to the end of the line if they wanted to make another call. You could hear them laughing and talking loudly on the payphone to their loved ones, inevitably explaining that the call was free, and that, no, there was no emergency and everyone was fine, and yes, they could talk to the kids too, and no, don't believe all you hear in the news, everyday life goes on in spite of the war.

Every once in a while, someone off the street would try one of the other two phones and come over to say, "You know the other phone works too?" At which point a couple of people newly in line would exclaim, "Does it?" and leave us to use the other phones, looking at us strange.

We smiled at one another, silently acknowledging the fact that this is best kept a secret: we didn't want too many people in the line, and we didn't want the authorities to suspect that something was wrong lest they fix it. I noticed a night attendant sitting on a chair up the stairs in front of the entrance to the phone center's main building. He was smoking a cigarette and reading a magazine. *He must know*, I thought.

You were supposed to insert a five rial coin into the slot to get a dial tone and dial the number. Once you hung up, the broken phone would give your coin back. People walking out of the booth would proudly wave their lucky five rial coin, getting a little cheer from the folks in line.

When Dariush finally made it to the booth and dialed his number out of a neat little notebook, he started speaking in English.

"Hello? He... Hello? Peppi?" He sounded excited. "Peppi? It's me... Dariush... Peppi?... Yes! Yes, my dear. How are you, my dear Peppi?... I love you, Peppi... I really love you, my dear Peppi... Yes, it's your Dariush... No, I am not in Portugal, I am in Iran. Oh, I miss you my dear Peppi..."

This went on for quite a while and really excited my imagination: who was Peppi? Was that a girl's name? Dariush had not been abroad since the revolution so they must have been apart for at least four years. *He looks nervous. Are his eyes welling up?*

Maman Bahram didn't say anything. She didn't even smile when Dariush finally walked out of the booth, all frustrated that the phone had not returned his five rial coin after talking to Portugal for a good ten minutes. I think she wasn't even listening. She had probably zoned out concentrating on what she'd say to Teri and the kids.

***

Teri and the kids had fled Iran last summer. Teri was Uncle Kourosh's blond and blue-eyed American wife. She was quite a feisty character. She spoke Farsi fluently, and had started a school for foreign students in Iran after the revolution. They had run the school for a year or two but last year, when we found out that my uncles were imprisoned, and after her school was shut down by the authorities, she had decided to leave, and had carried out her plan without letting anyone know.

We were up north one day when Baba Javad, my grandfather, called us and said that he had gone to Uncle Kourosh's house to check on them and had found the place empty, Teri and the kids gone. We had been very worried but found out from one of the neighbors that she had meant to leave the country.

We found out later that she had paid a human trafficker to take them across the border to Turkey, and that they had done so wearing sheepskins and pretending to be part of a herd. I'm not quite sure why they did it that way. I don't think their lives were threatened. They probably needed Uncle Kourosh's permission to leave, but why wouldn't he give them that? Whatever it was, something had snapped for her, and she had made up her mind to flee. And when Teri made up her mind to do something, she did it.

***

When our turn came to use the broken payphone, it was almost one in the morning, and we were amongst the last people in line, along with only a few families waiting patiently behind us. Dariush had long said goodbye and left, and everything was a bit more serious and less smiley with my grandma and Uncle Kourosh now.

Uncle Kourosh dialed Teri's number and handed the phone to Maman Bahram.

"Teri! Teri, I'm so happy to hear your voice," she said. "How are you? How are the kids? Yes, I'm OK, thank you. Listen... Teri... When will you come back?"

I think I heard my Uncle's tsk-tsk.

Maman Bahram, being the romantic that she was, wanted everyone back together again. She wanted Teri to return, for Uncle Kourosh and Teri to be in love, and for their love to motivate them to fight the realities of the world and to get them back together again here in Iran. She was hopeful. She was still hopeful. Her son, Uncle Siamak, had not been executed yet.

"It is very good here... Yes... Yes... No... America not good, Iran good... We love you, Teri... When will you come back, huh?"

Uncle Kourosh was visibly uncomfortable but he didn't say anything. He was probably craving one of his Cuban's and a big coffee.

"Teri...? Teri...? I think she hung up? Oh! Turaj? Is that you?

Teri was probably not very comfortable with Maman Bahram's insistence and had passed the phone to her older son, Turaj.

"Turaj *Farsi yaadet hast*? Turaj...?" She turned to me. "Babak, here, you talk to him." She handed me the phone.

I played the real-time translator, going back and forth between English and Farsi. "We miss you... Tell your mom to bring you home.... I've knitted you a really nice blue pullover, the color of your eyes... You should get your Mom to speak Farsi with you..."

She finally ceded the phone to Uncle Kourosh, but as soon as he started talking, the connection dropped and the coin was duly returned.

"You guys go to the car," he said to us. "I'll wait my turn and try again."

We sat in Uncle Kourosh's car watching the short line proceed slowly and waiting for Uncle Kourosh's turn.

"She still loves him," Maman Bahram said, staring ahead, half to herself.

"Who?"

"Teri," she said. "Teri still loves Kourosh."

She thought about it some more. "This is good. I'm glad they're talking. Things will get better. They'll come home."

I looked at her face. This was how my atheist grandmother prayed. She wished and willed, with all her might, for the world to change back to where it was in happier times, when we all gathered in the front yard to say goodbye to Jamshid, Dariush's little brother, who was leaving to study in Paris. Dad captured it in a farewell photograph. Everyone was there: Uncle Siamak, with squinting eyes, Jamshid, with a newspaper under his elbow, Uncle Bahram, handsome and quiet, pulling my cheeks, Uncle Kourosh, carrying Turaj, standing next to Teri, Baba Javad, smiling his radiant smile, truly happy, and my mom, smiling too, radiantly at the camera. And Maman Bahram, in the back, staring into the future, knowing that this happy extended family would not come together again for a while, but having faith in that, if she had anything to do with it, eventually, it would.

Uncle Kourosh finally made it to the booth. Everyone had left by now and it was just him talking to his children and wife in America. At first, he was frowning, but a few minutes into the conversation, a rare, wide smile broke out on his face.

"He loves her," Maman Bahram whispered.

My mind was cloudy, having been fighting to stay awake for the past hour or so. The setting was like a strange dream: there was no one on the usually crowded Paasdaaraan Street. No traffic either. We were the only car parked by the curb, and there was a man in one of three phone booths—my Uncle Kourosh—we were staring at.

"Oh! Oh!" Maman Bahram nudged me.

I was so focused on Uncle Kourosh's facial expressions that it took me a moment to pan out and realize what was going on. The phone booth was surrounded by gunmen with AK-47s, closing in on Uncle Kourosh, and there were more pouring out of two military station wagons. Where did these guys come from? Uncle Kourosh had not realized what was happening and was still talking on the phone, laughing.

"Sir! Sir!" The men kept calling, but Uncle Kourosh was ignoring them.

"Oh my God!" Maman Bahram grasped my hand and was pressing it hard. Two of the soldiers were pointing their guns at my uncle.

Finally, Uncle Kourosh said his goodbyes and stepped out of the booth with his hands raised, still smiling.

"Oh my God! What are they doing?"

"They're patting him down, Maman Bahram," I said, trying to sound reassuring. "They'll realize they've made a mistake and let him go."

Uncle Kourosh talked to them for a few minutes and pointed at our car a couple of times. The revolutionary guard that seemed to be senior to the rest of them gave orders, and some of the men got in one of the station wagons and left.

Uncle Kourosh talked to the guy some more and he finally headed to our car.

"Oh, thank God!" Maman Bahram said.

Uncle Kourosh got in the driver's seat. "Maman, please go sit in the back."

"What's going on? What do they want?" Maman Bahram's fear came out as anger and I wished she'd just cooperate.

"Maman, just…" He pointed, and Maman Bahram, frowning, went to the back seat as she mumbled under her breath in disappointment.

The guard with his machine gun got in the front seat and started giving Uncle Kourosh directions. He seemed to be pretty young, maybe no more than eighteen, maybe younger, with a kind country face and green eyes.

"Where are you taking us?" Maman Bahram asked him.

"We're going to HQ," he said. "Don't worry."

"But what's the charge?" Maman Bahram asked. "We haven't done anything wrong."

"The phone was broken, you know," Uncle Kourosh said, in a softer more cooperative tone. "Lots of people have been using it to make free phone calls since this afternoon. We just happened to be the last in line."

"Free, huh?" the guard asked with a smirk.

"That's not our fault. The Telecom is responsible," Maman Bahram said.

"Don't worry… Turn here," the guard said.

We stopped at a gate and the soldier nodded at the guard, who opened it for us. We parked the car and walked into a building with a long, narrow corridor. He opened a door and we entered a room.

"Give me your driver's license," he said to Uncle Kourosh. "Don't worry," he said again before he shut the iron door and locked it from the outside.

The room was empty except for a bench. The concrete walls were painted boy's-room blue. There were no windows and the room was lit by a dull fluorescent lamp on the ceiling.

I was scared.

This was prison. We had been thrown into jail and they had locked the door on us. Uncle Bahram was in prison and we'd just heard that he'd gotten a five-year sentence for going to the movies on the wrong day. The last time Uncle Kourosh was imprisoned he'd been there for a month before we even found out, and they'd kept him for nine months without charge. I didn't like it here. I had school tomorrow. I had a bad feeling in my stomach and felt like I needed to use the toilet.

They must think this is a serious case of espionage with Uncle Kourosh passing secret information to the CIA from a non-descript phone booth on Paasdaaraan. We will be interrogated and tortured. We will break under pressure and they'll film us giving false testimony about being members of the Mossad and MI6 and the KGB. Our minimum sentence would be execution by firing squad after 70 lashes.

All this while Maman Bahram was being angry, and Uncle Kourosh was trying to calm her down with reasoning, and it wasn't working.

"Kourosh, they have no right to do this. We should call a lawyer." Maman Bahram had a big frown on her face.

"A lawyer?" Uncle Kourosh laughed. He seemed genuinely relaxed. "You think you're in Europe? This is the revolutionary guard."

"We should ask them to take us to their commanding officer. This is not right." Maman Bahram shook her head.

"Calm down, Maman. They've made a mistake and they'll let us go. We'll just have to let them save face."

"Save face?" Maman Bahram said with fury. "They need to apologize." And then to herself, "Save face he says." She chuckled.

"Just let me handle it, Maman."

I wish she'd stop. Just let him handle it. We need to listen to Uncle Kourosh and stop arguing. He knows what he's doing. He's experienced.

I felt cold. Was this place colder than outside? I really, really wanted to go home. I craved my soft bed and warm blanket. And my parents.

Maman Bahram fell silent for a few minutes. Uncle Kourosh was deep in thought. Then she started over, and they fell into another cycle of pointless arguing.

I tried blocking it out by playing with my LCD watch. I kept looking at the time, trying to imagine what was going on at home. Was Mom worried yet? Had she woken Dad up yet? Were they too arguing about whether it was time to worry about us or not? Siamak and Sara would be fast asleep. Or maybe they'd pretend to be sleeping but they'd be listening to the argument and worrying too.

I started playing with the digital watch's nifty liquid crystal chronometer. We had invented some games with Hakim, my high school friend. One was to see if we could stop the timer at exactly eleven seconds and eleven hundredth of a second. After getting bored with that, I played speed-stopping: Basically, you started and stopped the chronometer as quickly as you could. My world record was six hundredth of a second, which I thought was pretty cool. I'd read somewhere that it takes a tenth of a second for the brain signal to get to the limbs, so using one finger to start and stop a timer that quickly was certainly in defiance of that. Another game was to use two fingers, one to start and the other to hit the lap button. My world record there was an amazing four hundredth of a second.

I must have played for a good half-hour or so, breaking my lap record by one hundredth of a second, and succeeding in blocking out everything, when the iron door to our cell was opened and a soldier called us to follow him.

"Where are you taking us?" Maman Bahram asked.

"Seyyed will see you now," the soldier said, knocking on a door and showing us in.

I was in a heightened state of worry, not as much for myself. I felt I knew how to get myself out of this, but I was worried about my uncle and my grandma. They were the grown-ups and I had no control over them. They would be considered guilty until proven innocent, and everything they'd say could be used against them, and I wasn't sure if either of them recognized the risk. I felt the lone realist in a world of idealistic revolutionaries. And I was thirteen.

A heavily bearded man of thirty was sitting at an empty desk, looking at what seemed to be Uncle Kourosh's driver's license. A large picture of a frowning Khomeini, the leader of the Islamic Revolution, was on the wall behind him. Uncle Kourosh and Maman Bahram sat at the two school chairs facing the desk and I was left lingering behind them.

My presence was completely ignored by everyone, it seemed.

"Mr. Zaim?" The Seyyed's voice was deep.

"Why don't you keep me and let them go?" Maman Bahram blurted.

Seyyed looked at her, somewhat surprised, and smiled, "Why? What have you done?"

"Nothing. Absolutely nothing," Maman Bahram said.

"Then why do you want to stay here?" he asked.

"Maman, please calm down," Uncle Kourosh said, and he turned to Seyyed. "Sir, what do you need from us?"

"He needs to save face 'cause they made a big mistake."

"Shh! Mom!"

Seyyed smiled again. "Tell me why you think you are here?"

"I think there's been a mistake. The phone was broken and we were making an international call."

"Whom were you calling?"

"My kids."

"And his wife." Maman Bahram was met with Uncle Kourosh's glare.

"What were you talking about?" Seyyed asked.

"Just talking. We hadn't talked for more than two years."

"Do you miss them?"

"Of course! They are my children."

"Why are they not here, Mr..." He looked at the driver's license again. "Mr. Zaim?"

"Good question," Maman Bahram whispered.

"My kids are at school there. Obviously, it is difficult for me to visit," Uncle Kourosh explained.

"I was trying to convince them to come back," Maman Bahram added.

Seyyed looked at her and smiled again. Maybe she reminded him of someone he knew. I liked this smile. Was he softening up?

"Why were you using the broken phone?" he asked.

"It was free!" Uncle Kourosh said.

"Was it?" he asked. "Someone must be paying for the calls you made, Mr. Zaim." He looked Uncle Kourosh in the eye. "Have you broken the law?"

"What? No!" Maman Bahram jumped out of her chair, furious. "We made a phone call, that's all!"

Seyyed didn't flinch, but his smile went away, and I didn't like that.

"Maman, why don't you sit down and let me talk?" Uncle Kourosh said quickly, then turned to Seyyed with an awkward smile. "She's very tired."

"Why did you break the law, Mr. Zaim?" Seyyed insisted.

"I don't understand, sir, how have we broken the law?" Uncle Kourosh asked calmly and politely.

"You have stolen from the people."

"Stolen?"

"Do you know the punishment for robbery in Islam?"

I grasped my hands behind my back. Of course, we all knew the punishment: amputation. Surely, he couldn't mean it though.

"We put coins in the phone but it returned them," I said with a shaky voice and close to tears.

Seyyed didn't even look at me. "You knowingly stole from the people and you have to pay for it."

"But we weren't the only ones who used that phone," Uncle Kourosh said.

"You are guilty, Mr. Zaim. It is as if you robbed a defenseless corpse lying in a dark alley."

"Fair enough," Uncle Kourosh replied. "I will pay if everyone else who used that phone also pays. Why should we be the only one punished?"

"Don't worry, Mr. Zaim, we will catch them." He was smiling again.

We could sense that a verdict was about to be announced. After a brief silence, during which Seyyed played with Uncle Kourosh's driver's license, he finally spoke up. His tone was different, softer, yet more forceful. "Mr. Zaim, you are guilty of stealing from the people, and until such time as your punishment is set…" my heart was pounding, "your car and driver's license will be held here as a guarantee of your return."

The sound of our collective exhale filled the room, louder than we'd wanted, but deep down I was elated. We were going home!

"Seyyed-jaan, how are we to go home? I need my car," Uncle Kourosh said, making me wish he'd just forego the darn car. Why push our luck, the guy was being kind to us and saving us from the dungeons and torture?

"I will stay, let them go." Maman Bahram was starting again.

Oh my God, what are these guys doing? Can I call my dad?

"No need, no need." Seyyed was clearly tired of the whole thing and thinking that he had better things to do. "You can take your car. I'll keep the driver's license."

"But—"

"Brother Mostafa!" Seyyed called out

The soldier, who must have been right outside the door, stepped in. "Yes, sir?"

"Show Mr. Zaim and his family to their car. They are free to go."

***

We got home at four-thirty in the morning. Mom was awake and waiting for us.

"Where have you been?" She clutched me firmly in her embrace.

I was so sleepy I left the story to be told by Maman Bahram, and went straight to bed. But I was too tired to sleep. I kept thinking of all the things that had happened that day and how I should tell it to Siamak when he woke up in the morning. In my mind, the images started getting muddled and mixed, and when I finally did fall asleep, I dreamed of being in prison with Dariush, and he seemed to know Seyyed from the past, and they were both smiling, and he kept calling him Peppi. That's funny; I thought Peppi was a girl's name.

HAPPY ENDING

*W*hen I was fifteen, we bought a Betamax VCR, and this was a big moment in my life. Since the beginning of the war, a few years prior, we had been in almost complete isolation from Western culture.

There was the BBC World Service, of course, which I listened to religiously, trying to keep up, but that was mainly news and some music on a crackling shortwave radio.

I had raided the local bookstore for secondhand paperbacks and read them all, but they had probably been left behind by folks who had long fled the country—and all the books and magazines were from before 1978.

After much pleading, my parents were finally convinced to buy the VCR when Dariush, my mom's cousin, said that he would provide the films.

In those days, video cassettes were illegal in Iran, and there were no video rentals. We only had two TV channels, neither of which had twenty-four-hour programming, and both of which were mostly political and religious shows, with occasional, heavily censored re-runs of boring old movies. A bootleg video network had recently emerged, however, with people like Dariush getting what they could in the latest movies and TV shows, recording them from VCR to VCR, and renting them out to people they trusted.

That was part of the reason why we loved to visit Aunt Makhsoos, Dariush's mom. She would let us watch the odd movie Dariush had left behind for her.

The problem was, Aunt Makhsoos insisted on only watching a certain kind of movie.

"Dariush, are you sure the movie has a happy ending?" she would ask.

"Yes, Maman."

"Have you checked?" she would insist. "You know I can't watch anything that doesn't have a happy ending."

"Yes, I know, Maman. I always check," Dariush would say, reassuringly. "The ending for this one is really happy."

We found it funny, given her insistence, how, once the movie was over, Aunt Makhsoos would express genuine astonishment at the happy outcome for all the characters.

"They married! They married! She accepted! They finally found each other. I was so worried she would say no, but she accepted! Unbelievable! What a great movie!"

***

Every week, Dariush would bring us three movies of his own selection. They were hidden in a brown paper bag, which he would then use to hide the three we were returning. The names of the movies, scribbled hastily on the jacket, were usually wrong, as the films were re-used repeatedly. Betamax was already pretty low quality, and re-recording films on the same tape would often make them unwatchable, even after running the VCR head-cleaning tape through the device several times. But raw video cassettes, though legal, were expensive and hard to come by.

It was great. We felt like we were back in the civilized world again, watching variety shows, new TV series, and the latest and greatest from Hollywood: *Tootsie, Scarface, War Games, Terms of Endearment, Flashdance!*

The whole family would huddle around the color TV in Maman Bahram's living room after Friday lunch to watch the latest, and if the film was good, we'd be talking about it until dinner.

Not everyone enjoyed the movies in the same way, of course.

My dad would make himself comfortable in front of the TV but would stay awake through the whole thing only if it was a nature documentary or something to do with classical music.

"That was a great movie, wasn't it?" he would say.

"But you slept right through it, Amir." Mom would laugh. "How do you know it was good?"

"It was good," he'd reply, smiling sheepishly. "I slept well."

My grandpa, Baba Javad, would watch the movies intently up until any point of high-tension conflict, a shootout, or an argument between the main characters. Then, while we were all completely absorbed in the story, he would ask, "Is this real, or are they just play-acting?"

"Of course, they're play-acting, Baba," Mom would explain, annoyed. "You think they would actually shoot someone for that scene?"

"They're play-acting!" Baba Javad would exclaim, disgustedly. "Now what is the meaning of that? What a waste of time." He'd then go do the dishes or pick up a crossword puzzle.

Later, he would sometimes ask me, from behind his thick glasses, if I enjoyed the movie.

"Yes, Baba Javad, it was pretty good."

He would frown and think about it for a moment. "But it's all made-up play-acting. I don't get the point of it." He would then shrug and go back to his newspaper.

One night, after having watched a really good movie, I sat there, thinking, as the credits rolled. Everyone had gone to bed, but I was still there listening to the ending music, imagining myself in a world where what I had just seen was the norm. Boys and girls could be friends and go out together. There was dancing and rock music, and girls were pretty, and they didn't have to cover their hair, and boys could grow their hair long and wear tight jeans and superhero t-shirts and jackets with shoulder pads, and everybody was happy.

The film rolled on after the credits, and static filled the screen. I was still staring at the TV, daydreaming with blurry eyes, when the picture flickered back on again. The sound came back on too and it was so loud,

I jumped for the clunky remote and hit MUTE, but the film stopped and started rewinding.

Click, brrrr...

What the heck was that? I thought, wide awake now. *Were those guys naked?*

I stopped the rewind and hit PLAY. It was back on the static again. I looked around to make sure I was alone and slowly got up and shut the TV room door.

The picture came back on again.

Wow!

The picture had some static and the quality was poor, but I could clearly make out a naked man and woman. She was turning toward the camera and revealing her breasts and, for a split second, her...

Click, brrrr...

Damn!

I stopped and played again, holding my finger on the pause button. It was tricky, but I had to stop the image just moments before the tape's end and the auto-rewind to get a better view. It took a few trials, but I finally got it.

I couldn't believe my luck. *That dark spot must be her pubic hair,* I thought. *Wow!*

I rewound the cassette, placed it in its jacket, and tiptoed to my bed, thinking I would probably not get much sleep that night.

***

From that day on, I would use every chance I had to sneak into the TV room alone and picture-search past the credits of every film Dariush brought us, just to make sure I wasn't missing any happy endings.

CHALK AND TRIANGLES

"**C**an you draw six equilateral triangles with only six straight lines?" Saeed asked Hakeem, as they stood at the blackboard after class.

I was fourteen, a high schooler now, in Tehran. The year was 1982. The war with Iraq was in its second year and the Islamic regime was in the midst of a clampdown on any opposition to its rule.

As I packed my bag at the end of class that day, I was wondering what was taking Hakeem so long to come up with the solution to what I thought was an easy problem.

Hakeem and I had become good friends that year, and we were both into building electronic circuits in our spare time, and had run into each other at Mehran Kit, the one place downtown were you could buy all sorts of transistors and capacitors. He was a really smart kid, and I had learned a lot from him in the few months we'd been hanging out together.

Whiz!

"Class is over, you nerds!" Javad had taken some chalks from the board and, taking cover behind the last row, was aiming at Hakeem's drawing on the board.

Whiz!

"Down with nerds!"

I walked up to the board, picked up a chalk, and counted my lines aloud as I drew the solution.

"Is this it?" I asked, but Saeed was busy telling Hakeem why his solution was wrong and ignored me.

Whiz!

"Hey, Saeed," I said, "Saeed, look, six lines."

He threw a glance at my drawing. "No." He turned back to Hakeem. "That's a star."

"But it's six equilateral triangles with six lines," I said. "Look."

Whiz!

A piece of chalk hit the board next to my star.

"Saeed, look man..." I suddenly felt a sharp sting on my ear. "Ow!"

I grabbed a handful of chalks, turned around, and started throwing them at Javad in rapid fire. He ducked behind the benches. I was angry at him and frustrated at Saeed for ignoring me.

"Saeed!" I called out to him as I threw the chalks one by one. "God... dammit... look... at... my... star!"

I turned and both Saeed and Hakeem had a look of dread on their faces. At first, I thought they were stunned by my sudden fit of rage, but then I realized they were looking past me.

"Are these my chalks or yours?" came a deep voice at the door. I swung around. It was the vice-principal, Mr. Saeedi, with his long, black beard, thick, frowning eyebrows, and penetrating eyes, standing at the door, staring at me with fury.

"Are these my chalks or yours?" he asked again, walking towards me. I didn't know the answer.

"Are these my chalks or yours?" He was towering over me now, all six feet of him, looking down.

"Yours?" I suggested, sheepishly.

Slap!

I felt a burning in my left cheek. I guess my answer had been wrong.

"These chalks are *your* chalks," he said. "They are here to help you win in the education front. Your fellow countrymen are dying in the war of the righteous against the oppressors, and you are destroying what they are dying for. You should be ashamed."

He looked at the board.

"What is this?" He pointed at the star.

"It's a—" I started, but he attacked the triangle, wiping it ferociously with both hands.

"Who drew this?" he asked.

"I did, sir," I said. "It's a math riddle."

"Stop lying, boy. Who put you up to this?" He held his hand up, threatening to hit me again.

"Please, sir! I'm really sorry." I was terrified. "He gave us a riddle and I was trying to solve it. Honest to God, sir. Please... I'm sorry." I felt a tear rolling down my cheek.

Mr. Saeedi turned to Saeed.

"He's right, sir," Saeed said. "I gave them a riddle and..."

Hakeem, standing next to him, nodded in confirmation. All this time he had stayed frozen, chalk in hand, halfway through his attempt to solve the riddle.

Mr. Saeedi looked at them, and then me, and I think he decided that we were innocent. His face broke into a patronizing smile, and he started clapping his hands together gently to get rid of the white chalk powder all over them.

"My dear kids," he said, "you should be more vigilant. Enemies of Islam are everywhere, trying to deceive you. Look how far they go, devising math riddles to make you unwanted tools of Zionists."

I didn't understand what he was saying. What did Israel have to do with all of this?

"Be vigilant." He softly touched my left cheek. "Islam needs you. Islam needs you to be vigilant, my brothers."

"Yes, sir," I said. "Really sorry, sir. We should be vigilant, sir."

He smiled and left the room.

***

"What was the fucking correct answer, then, Saeed?" I asked a few minutes later, after the big lump in my throat had subsided enough for me to be able to talk. "Do you even know yourself?"

"Not the star, Babak, I swear it's not the Star of David." Saeed picked up a chalk and drew the correct answer on the blackboard.

I counted the lines and the triangles. He was right.

"Interesting," Hakeem said. "But Babak's solution is correct, too. The problem has two correct answers and I got neither. How depressing."

We all laughed and packed our things.

"So," I said, as we turned the lights off and left the class, "what is this star of David?"

THE KISS

W hen I was a teenager, at my friend Behzad's place one day, we were sitting in a circle playing spin the bottle with his sister, Neda, and her pretty friend. This round, the 'penalty' was a kiss on the lips. I was 'it' and the bottle was spinning, and I was hoping upon hope that it would end up pointing at her. Kissing my friend would have been yucky, and kissing his sister with Behzad being there would have been weird.

Of course, I had been kissed on the cheek many times. And I had even French-kissed, sure. In fact, there's a photo of me holding my teddy bear, kissing a girl, seemingly on her lips. It's a cute photo. We are one-year-olds, probably put up to it by our parents, and I was likely going for her cheek but she swung around and we made contact in a very wet smooch somewhere halfway on the lips, halfway on the cheek. But I didn't remember it, and most probably didn't appreciate it at the time.

Oh, how I yearned to experience it. Kissing a girl. On the lips. What would it feel like? Would I like it? Would she like it? Would I be good? What do you do, really, when you kiss someone on the lips? I mean, the mechanics are bound to be different, right? You can't be sucking in too much. You don't want to make it gross and suck in her saliva. I mean, kissing a cheek is easy. It's just skin, waiting there to be kissed. It won't be kissing back. What if you get it wrong?

I had tried practicing it once, late at night, on the wall next to my bed, pretending the slight crack in the paint was a girl's mouth. I closed my eyes and kissed, trying to keep my lips on hers, and then switching around to make it perpendicular to her mouth, trying to remember to open my mouth at the same time, because you don't want to do it that way with both mouths shut or you'll end up catching her nose, which would be awkward.

The experience was utterly dissatisfying. Learning my side of the deal without having someone on the other end simply did not work.

The bottle stopped at me again, as we sat in a circle on the wooden tiled floor of Behzad's living room, and so we spun it one more time, harder. The darned thing wouldn't stop. My brain was racing with worry. What if it did stop at her? What would I do? I had no practice and I'd managed to play it cool so far, and I thought I'd left a good impression on her and if I screwed this kiss up, I would be screwing our friendship up before it even started. What if she was the one? What if we were destined to fall madly in love and run away from home and get married in a far-off land?

The bottle stopped. It was pointing squarely at her. This was it. All the excited noises Behzad and Neda were making muted into the background of my head. We moved up to each other and brought our heads close. I could feel her breath on me. She tilted her head a bit. *Good idea*, I thought, *so this is how you avoid the noses bumping*. She closed her eyes and perked her lips. They looked small, sweet, symmetrical, delicate, and inviting. I kept my eyes open as I closed in carefully on the last inch, and then our lips touched. The bump in the middle of her upper lip was the first touch point, slipping as it rubbed gently against mine. And the point of contact grew to include most of her lips. It was a soft sensation. And warm. Warmer than I'd expected. And a bit moist. It was alive, and sensitive. It reacted to my lips in a very subtle way, but I felt it. It was all I felt. I closed my eyes and, for that split second, my entire being was focused on where my lips met hers. We didn't press too hard. Just enough to squeeze together without getting to the hardness of our teeth. Then we disengaged, ever so slightly, to produce the softest of smacks that only the two of us heard. I felt a smooth wave spread through my face and my skin and to every follicle of hair in my body, alerting every cell of the significance of that moment. It was strange. It was delightful. It was beautiful. I liked it.

We both pulled back and opened our eyes giggling with a slight blush. Just before returning to our childish spinning game, I caught her gaze and she caught mine. We were probably both wondering what the other felt. Was it as precious and wonderful an adventure for her as it was for me? I had just experienced the ultimate point in two humans being kind and respectful and in harmony with one another.

As I walked home that night, I reviewed the whole thing in my head over and over again, promising myself never to forget how it felt to kiss a girl on the lips for the first time.

HAIRCUT

I keep my hair short. It's easier this way. Saves me time under the
shower, and I don't need to comb: less stress. I think short hair
calms me down. These days, as soon as I can hold the tip of my hair
in a pinch, I head to the barber's and have it machined, number 2, all
around.

It wasn't always like this. In fact, come to think of it, my hair used
to be a big concern for me back in the day. I used to crave that feeling of
warmth on the back of my neck and over my ears. It gave me confidence.
The breeze, blowing through it from the correct angle, moved the
camera of my self-consciousness to look up at me, showing me as a proud
Persian warrior gazing at the distant horizon, with a hint of a smile,
acknowledging the admiration of all the beautiful women I'd ever loved.

Actually, life used to be a struggle when it came to hair. Mine is the
soft, limp kind that just faints around my head in whatever direction
gravity pulls it. As a child, my mom always kept it short, and in my list of
evil places, the barbershop came in second place, right after the dentist's.
After Iran's revolution, having to wear our hair short at school was one of
few things in the Islamic regime my mom secretly appreciated.

I'm not sure why long hair was banned. It might have been a reaction to the fashion of the '80s. Might have been homophobia. Hair was an important priority in the Islamic republic. The hijab had been made mandatory for women, and long hair was banned for men. Find excuses to restrict individual liberties–Subjugation 101.

My entry into college, fall of '85, gave me a sense of freedom. No more strict school dress code, I started wearing jeans and short-sleeve shirts, and, fulfilling my lifelong dream, I grew my hair all the way to my shoulders. I don't know if it made me look good, but it certainly made me feel confident, and I loved the reaction I got from friends seeing me with the new look. I'm not sure if my mom liked it, though.

I remember my excitement to see my buddy Bijan. He lived in the Shomal, and I hadn't seen him for a couple of years. Now, at last, during our first break from university and free from the stress of having to pass the entrance exams, we were up north with my family, enjoying the lush tropical weather of the Caspian Sea.

We had just arrived the previous night and I took my dad's car to find Bijan, when a freakin' revolutionary guard on a motor bike pulled me over and asked for my ID.

He was a big man in typical nondescript military khakis, almost too big for his Suzuki minibike. Mean-looking, with a round face, a thick beard, and a buzz cut.

"I thought you were a girl!" He squinted at my student ID.

"I'd be wearing a hijab if I were a girl."

He ignored that. Long pause, as he contemplated with a frown. He was just doing that for effect. But he was good at it.

"You go to Sharif?"

"Yes, sir," I said, and started keeping time in my head, trying to see if he was doing the same.

After exactly five seconds, he said, "Good school. Just got in, didn't you?"

"Yes, sir." One one thousand, two one thousand…

"Fighting for the revolution on the education front, are you…?"

I smiled broadly, but he was not smiling.

"…looking like this?" He looked at me disapprovingly. I folded my arms, thinking maybe the short sleeves were offending him. He looked disgusted. "In the Islamic Republic, it is not becoming of a young student to wear his hair so long." He slid my ID into his shirt pocket. "You will cut your hair." He looked at me with deep disdain as I sat stunned and immobile. Then he got on his bike and drove off.

Oh my God, I need to cut my hair quickly. He's going to lose my card and I'll be halfway to the front before anyone can prove I'm a student.

The Iran-Iraq War was raging and there were many horror stories about students who didn't have their ID cards on them at a checkpoint and had been boarded on a bus to the front right there and then. That ID was the only thing keeping me from being a soldier at war.

I had to get a haircut quickly and come find this guy while he was still on the street, or who knew where my ID would end up? I didn't even know if he was a *Basiji* paramilitary or *Komiteh-ee* revolutionary police, or maybe the actual police force. Where was he based? He may have been from any number of units around here, or just visiting for the holidays. Came here from some far-off town, doing a few rounds before lunch to rack up on his virtuous deeds count. I had nothing on him, and he had my precious card.

After circling the town a couple of times in search of a barbershop, I hurried back home and found my mom, playing solitaire in the living room, listening to the radio.

"Mom, I need a haircut and all the barbershops are closed."

"Of course. It's a holiday, honey." She noticed my pale and worried face. "What happened?"

"A guard took my ID. Because of the hair."

"Oh dear! I keep telling you to cut it!" Somehow urgency always slowed my mom down.

"Can you cut it for me?"

"But I'm not a barber!" She got up, looking worried.

"Please! Just cut the back so I can show him I'm serious about having it cut. I need that ID back!"

I found a plain brown long-sleeve shirt and quickly pulled it over the happy-red short-sleeve I already had on.

"You shouldn't let it get to this in the first place," she said as she went to the kitchen to find a pair of scissors. "Now where's the morning paper? Don't want to make a mess."

"Just cut the back." Her calm was irritating me.

"OK."

She held my hair tightly in her hand, pulled it down, and started cutting as short as she could. That's when it started sinking in. Every snip was a sour reminder of what it had taken to grow it. All that effort, all that patience, tolerating the awkward sidewinders over my ears, the double-checks in the mirror twenty times a day, the constant indecision to part it on the side or in the middle, the hard work to get it to finally be how it should be… all of that going away with a few simple bites of the scissors.

I ran out of the house as soon as I saw the big chunk of hair in her fist.

No time to waste. I jumped in the car and zoomed away, trying to forget what I was leaving behind. I noticed my buddy Bijan hanging out on the street corner, and I pulled over. I was glad to see him. He was a local and there was a chance he knew the guy who took my card.

"Hey you're back! What the heck did you do to your hair?" He got in the car.

"A guard took my ID. You need to help me find him. He's a big fellow; round face. I think his name tag read 'Esfandiari' or something like that."

"Don't know him. He's probably not from around here."

"Darn!"

He thought for a moment, then gestured for me to make a left turn. "Let's go to the dairy store. They may know him."

We stopped a couple of blocks down the street towards town.

This was a new store and I'd never been to it before. There was no one at the counter. I was restless to get on with our quest.

"Where are they? Shouldn't we just go back to town now? He can't be far. This was barely ten minutes ago."

"Hello?" he called out, ignoring me.

"Coming!" came a reply from a sweet young lady's voice in the back.

I looked at Bijan, and something in his smile told me we were here for more than what I'd thought.

The girl finally showed up and I froze in place as soon as I saw her: she was the prettiest thing I'd ever seen. Beautiful, smiling eyes, light brown hair peeking through a pink scarf she tied behind her head, showing off the smoothest, nicest neck.

I suddenly noticed she was approaching me, looking at me with kind, caressing eyes.

"This is terrible!" she was exclaiming in a soft Shomali accent. Bijan must have explained the situation to her while I was in a state of bedazzlement, and she was looking at my hair, which was long all in the front but cut abruptly in the back. I had misread her look: it was one of pity, and now she was blushing and almost holding back her laughter.

I must look hideous, I realized for the first time. I felt terrible. I buttoned up my shirt quickly, trying to hide the collar of the red one underneath. I wanted to liquefy and pour out of the center of that embarrassing attention into a drain to the sea. Why did this have to have happened now? How could I erase this image from her brain? How could I ever come back and ask for her hand? Why did Bijan bring me here? I hated him!

"Come on." Bijan pushed me out.

"What?"

"Didn't you hear her? The guard is still roaming in the center square. Let's go, man!"

We jumped in the car and whizzed towards town. I was driving super-fast, partly to get away from her.

Sure enough, once we got to the center square, we found the big guy on his motor bike. He'd stopped a car and was checking the passenger's ID. I brought the car to a screeching halt, blocking his bike, and that gave him a jump. He turned to us, going for his gun. It took him a moment to recognize me.

"Can I get my ID back, please?"

He squinted at me saying nothing.

"Um, I need my ID, please; I think it's in your front pocket."

"What have you done?" He pointed at his own head.

"The barbershops were closed. My mother cut it."

"This is terrible!" He seemed genuinely concerned, looking at my hair with distaste.

"Please…" It was warm and my throat seemed to be pushing at my tightly buttoned double collar now.

"No, this is not good."

"But I cut it!"

"No. You need to fix it and come back."

I could not believe my ears. I fought hard to hide the frustration in my voice. "Come on. I'll shave it tomorrow, I promise!" I was really not enjoying this conversation and didn't want to be seen begging in public wearing that embarrassing hairdo. "May I get my ID back, please?" I was desperate.

In my mind, he froze, and in a slow-motion instant, I had a flash image of my recurring nightmare: It was me, as seen from the lower left side, crouching on one knee behind a dirt hill, easing my head up slowly as I aim my heavy AK-47 out into the unknown of enemy fire. It is dry and dusty; the scorching sun is hurting my eyes. I am sweaty, and everything smells like gunpowder. It makes me feel queasy.

"It's ugly!" His voice brought me back. With a big frown, he reached into his front pocket and found my card out of the five or six he drew out. He looked at both sides carefully. I stood still, holding my breath. Finally, after an eternity—or five seconds—he reached half-out and handed back my precious ID card.

I snatched it out of his hand, jumped in the car, leaving Bijan in my wake, and drove home to hide until first thing in the morning the next day, when I'd get a buzz cut for the first time in my life.

I've never worn my hair that long since. I always keep it short. It's easier this way.

THE STATS PROFESSOR

*Y*assai was relatively short, bearded, with thinning, curly gray hair, thick glasses, and a high-pitched voice. Nothing about his appearance was particularly strange, but he'd been rumored to have come to the campus in his underpants one time.

"I'm collecting stats on how people would react," he'd allegedly explained.

Dr. Yassai was a rather strange fellow. He was one of two statistics professors at Tehran's Sharif University in the mid-eighties during my time there as a software engineering undergrad.

When I asked Uncle Bahram, he remembered Yassai from before the revolution. Uncle Bahram is eleven years older than me, but at the time, we were both in our junior year at Sharif. He'd started thirteen years before, but his studies had been interrupted by the Cultural Revolution and his five years of imprisonment, having been falsely accused of rebellion against the regime. He'd only just received permission to go back to school.

"I had Stats 101 with him," he said.

"Cool! Did you get a good grade?"

"I got 20 out of 20," he replied. "He's kinda funny though."

"How so?" I asked.

"Well, for weeks after the final exam, after all the other professors had posted their test results, we got nothing from him. When we finally asked him, he said, 'Oh! I've posted them on my window.'" He laughed.

"So?" I couldn't see the humor in that. Most professors posted their grades on their room windows or doors.

"His room is on the fourth floor," he said, tears coming to his eyes, he was laughing so hard. "You'd need binoculars to read them."

I asked my buddy Keikhosro about him. He'd taken Stats 101 the previous year, and explained my choices as follows:

"If you want to really learn statistics but risk getting a low grade, go with Dr. Zaakaani. If you want to have fun and a good grade and don't care much about statistics, then Yassai is your man."

When I told Uncle Bahram's story to Keikhosro, all I got from him was a chuckle. Keikhosro was like that. He was what we used to call non-linear. You could never quite predict his reactions to things.

"Yeah," he said, matter-of-factly. "He's kinda non-linear."

"Dude, that's beyond non-linear," I said. "Sounds like the guy's totally lost it."

"Did you know he's got a couple of theorems to his name?" he asked. "Really?"

"Yeah, and not just any theorem. I ran into it when I was flipping through the book they use to teach post-grad level advanced stats at the math department."

That remark pretty much made my mind up for me.

***

The Stats 101 class was in the Ebnesina building, in the center of the campus. Ebnesina was a strange place. This building had changed names after the revolution, from the university's monarchist founding dean, Mojtahedi, to the Persian for Avicenna.

For starters, the dreaded room 21 was located there. You'd get called to room 21 if you had disciplinary issues. For boys, this meant you'd probably worn short sleeves or a t-shirt with English writing on it. Mostly, however, it was girls who got called up, their crimes ranging from laughing out loud, wearing make-up, or showing some hair, to sitting in the area designated as the boys' sitting area. There seemed to be a direct relationship between beauty and the number of times a girl got called to room 21, and in our class, Ladan held the world record.

Ladan was pretty. Not sure how she looked without the hijab, and sometimes girls would look very different with and without it, but in her light blue veil, and with her ever-smiling face, she had managed to break many hearts on campus. I had talked to her a couple of times, exclusively on study-related subjects. I wouldn't have minded her as a friend, but I didn't have any special feelings towards her. Perhaps that was why she seemed more comfortable talking to me than to the rest of the boys.

Ladan and I both entered Sharif at the same time; we studied software engineering, sharing many classes and experiences together, but we never talked more than a few sentences throughout the ten or so years that I knew her.

Anyway, I digress. Ebnesina was an interesting building. Every once in a while, I heard a story about some student—usually a girl—having committed suicide upon failing some course, throwing herself off the sixth floor. Sharif was, and still is, famous for being, academically, very strict, and that made these stories all the more believable.

The building had three stairways, one through the middle, and one on each side. One of the side stairways somehow managed not to go to the fourth floor and above, and I kept forgetting which one it was, forcing me to backtrack all the way down and up the other side to get to my classes.

The building also had a decent restroom, for a while the only one we knew of on the whole campus, and for that reason, amongst many of my fellow Sharif alumni, 'going to Ebnesina' became the unfortunate synonym for having to go to the restroom.

One time, as I was talking to a friend, waiting outside one of the rooms in Ebnesina for my class to begin, I felt a strange tension where my glasses rested on my nose. I stopped talking and suddenly one of the lenses exploded out.

"What happened?" my friend asked.

I took my glasses off and checked. "Did you see that?"

"What?"

"The lens just exploded!"

"What?"

"Look!" I showed him the empty frame.

We looked around and, save for some white powdery substance on the ground, we could not find any trace of the glass lens that had been correcting my left eye's vision up until a few moments ago.

***

My Stats 101 class with Dr. Yassai was held in the Ebnesina building. On the first day of classes, which coincided with some religious occasion, after picking the wrong stairway and backtracking to get myself to the classroom on the fourth floor, I found myself entering the class behind Ladan. The lecture had already started, a good five minutes early, before a seemingly empty class, as the students filed in.

"What the heck?" I whispered, half to myself. "Are we late?"

"Yassai," Ladan explained in a whisper, half to herself.

It took me a while to tune in and understand the monotonic and almost incomprehensible drawl emanating from the professor. He was short and potbellied with a scruffy, grey beard, thick glasses, thinning hair, a round head, and ears that stuck out like Alfred E Newman's. He was standing, sideways, somewhat tilted to the right of the podium, staring out of his thick glasses at a point on the floor a few feet to his left, almost speaking to himself.

"...and God almighty who bestowed our beloved Prophet the power of representing him in this world, and willed that we should not be left without religious guidance, which was bestowed to Ali, son of Abitaaleb, whose reign was just, and whose sword was..."

I tuned out for a few minutes, trying to decide if this was the same classroom in which I had had Database 101 last spring. That was when the racket from a couple of pigeons copulating just outside the window had amplified through the A/C duct, making it very hard for us to keep a straight face, let alone make out what the lecturer, who was completely ignoring the whole thing, was saying.

Refocusing my attention to Dr. Yassai's drawl, I suddenly noticed that he'd somehow managed to seamlessly change the subject from his little religious sermon to the stats course requirements, half of which I seemed to have missed.

"...which will earn you sixty percent of your final score and the other five percent will be based on your completing all the homework which I will assign to you after each class."

After a full hour of Dr. Yassai speaking with the same tone of voice, standing in the exact same spot, and with the exact same expression on his face, he stopped, rather abruptly, and walked out of the classroom.

The students looked at each other, not quite knowing what to make of this, and after a brief pause, we decided that the lecture was probably over, and began leaving.

"I didn't understand most of what he said," I remarked, half to myself.

"They say he gives out good grades," Ladan said, also speaking half to herself.

***

As it turned out, that first day was a prototype for every single class we had with the Doctor. No matter how early I got there, he'd always manage to be in the classroom and to have already started on his incomprehensible drawl of a lecture, starting with some religious topic of the day and merging seamlessly into the science of statistics.

Sometimes, he'd get very emotional about a topic.

"A normal distribution is within the realm of heavenly will, but a uniform distribution…" he'd raise his voice and go red in the face, "is sinful and ungodly and should be avoided!"

Somehow, he seemed to find a very real analogy between statistics and his religious worldview.

"A probability of one can only be assigned to God, while zero is evil," he said, in his introduction to probabilities, making me think that he was taking statistics to be the reality rather than the model. I've since met people who believe the nature of things to be based on mathematics and probabilities, so maybe, in his own crazy way, he was actually right.

A month or so into the term, I lost interest in the nutty professor and stopped attending altogether. I wasn't learning anything in his class anyway. None of my friends had the course, and even Ladan had stopped going after the third week. It wasn't as if he'd even realize if the class was completely empty; although there were always a fixed set of nerdy students who would attend, no matter what.

This wasn't the first course I'd skipped class for during college, but it was the first that I considered as a subject that I couldn't afford to ignore, and that I'd have to learn some other way. It was too important for the career path I'd already chosen by my sophomore year, namely, artificial intelligence.

There were, of course, many mandatory religious and revolutionary courses for which I'd taken pride in skipping class. My world record was a course by the name of 'Islamic Revolution and its Roots.' I managed not to attend a single class, playing basketball with Keikhosro instead. I'm lying. I did attend the class one time, but as soon as I took my seat, Keikhosro, who didn't have the course, showed up at the door and simply smiled at me, tilting his head slightly to the right, which was enough to drag me out of the classroom to follow him to the gym.

I did have a scare at the end of that course, though. I'd borrowed and studied Alexander's notes. He'd taken the course the year before. Only then had I found out what this course was all about: the Iranian Constitutional Revolution of eighty years ago, retold and changed from the Islamic Republic's perspective.

The final test only had four questions, but none had anything to do with the Constitutional Revolution! They were all about the nationalization of the oil industry in the '50s. It turns out that the professor had moved forward in time every term and Alexander's notes were useless. Fortunately, I knew a lot about Mosadegh and the '50s, and I had heard the Islamic Republic's version of events plenty of times to be able to eke out a C to pass the course.

Not all classes were that easy to skip though. The Mullah that taught 'The History of Islam' always had a paper on his desk that had to be signed by all students present. I had that course with Keikhosro and Alexander, and we took turns signing up for each other.

One time, we decided all to attend class. We sat at the very back and got quite bored with the Mullah's detailed account of how the Prophet's great-grandfather was a saint and all the great things he'd done, and so we started playing 'connect-the-dots.'

This is a game I used to play as a kid with my dad, where you put a bunch of dots in neat rows on a paper, and each player has to connect two adjacent dots with a line. If the line completes a square, then you put your initials in it and it counts as a point, and you get a bonus connection to make.

At a certain point in the game, I noticed that there was no way I could win, no matter which dots I connected, but that, depending on my move, I could make either Keikhosro or Alex win. Sitting in between the two, I looked at each with a smile, and gestured to them with my hands to pay up if they wanted to win. This made them both burst into laughter, and the class went utterly silent except for the Mullah, who was continuing on with his lecture, but when we tuned in to what he was saying, we noticed that he was actually making a remark about the class now.

"...and so, isn't it obvious that laughing in a class with a holy subject matter means laughing at the subject matter, and therefore could be considered ridiculing the Prophet's family, and by extension, the Prophet himself, and so be a clear example of blasphemy?"

"Are you referring to me, professor?" asked a student in the second row who had been listening intently and taking notes throughout the class.

The professor was staring through him at us, smiling, with his eyes squinting.

"Are you referring to me, professor?" the second-row student asked again.

"You know full well who I am referring to," the Mullah said.

"Are you referring to me, professor?" the annoying student asked again.

"I am referring to the gentleman who has his hand under his chin," the professor said, raising his voice a bit, and as soon as he said it, the three of us guiltily dropped our hands from under our chins. "Denying you your grades for this course, gentlemen, is the least I can do to appease the Almighty. The rest is up to you and the sincerity of your prayers of repentance."

I must admit, that sounded pretty scary, but as soon as he went back to his lecture, I started putting dots on the other side of the paper for another round.

***

Yassai posted the Stats 101 end-of-term grades on the announcement board on the first floor of the math department that year. There was a big crowd gathered around the board looking up their numbers when I got there, and they looked mostly disappointed.

"What the heck?" I let out as soon as I spotted my grade of 12.5 out of 20.

"It's pretty bad," a familiar voice said, and I turned around to find Ladan. She looked worried.

"I thought I did well." I turned back to the list. The better half of the class had been flunked, and the best grade was, in my newly acquired statistician's parlance, an outlier, at 17, with all other grades below 13.

"The distribution of the grades is normal, and therefore godly," someone said, mockingly.

"This is not acceptable!" Ladan was blushing with rage and sounding rather upset. She marched into the building and up the stairs.

I followed her in. I'd been counting on a high grade on stats to help with my GPA. I didn't know Ladan's grade, but judging by her reaction, she may have flunked.

There was a little crowd of ten to fifteen boy students at Dr. Yassai's door, grumbling amongst themselves, and knocking on the door every once in a while. Ladan was standing on the side, with red eyes and a seething look, staring at the door. Seeing her, I changed my mind and decided not to walk up to her to sympathize. I can deal with a girl's sadness, but I'd learned my lesson about angry girls.

The door swung open without warning, and the short, stout figure of the professor appeared, with his usual serious look on his round and scruffy face.

The students started complaining. "The grades seem to be wrong, sir!"

"You flunked most of the class!"

"Please reconsider, sir, the grades are too low."

He stood there staring at a point on the floor a few feet away to his left, talking in his usual low monotone, forcing everyone to stop and listen.

"...creation of all plants and animals into a world of plenty to live in harmony and Adam and Eve were moved to earth from heaven, to benefit from the potential riches but to have to work for their living and withstand the seasons and floods and earthquakes, and the past four seasons it happened that the grades were high and the riches were plenty, but this was not statistically sustainable and the distribution of grades had to be normalized with a left tail which was timely and statistically acceptable and thus the balance of God's love in creation is maintained and he is the almighty and the all-merciful."

He stepped back and shut the door on his stunned audience.

***

By the time I got my report card, my 12.5 in statistics had changed to a 0. I was studying software engineering, a brand-new subject in the '80s, with a brand-new department at my university, and the pre-requisites for courses kept changing every few terms. The recently computerized report card system used the latest course pre-requisite system, and so missed the nuances of the order by which we had actually taken the courses. This would typically result in zeroes for courses the computer thought were taken without the proper pre-requisite. I planned to fix this on the first day of the new term, but my plans were rudely interrupted by Scud Missiles.

***

After the first year of the Iran-Iraq War, neither side was able to win the upper hand in the fighting at the fronts. The Iranian side, having withstood the initial aggression, either thought they had a shot at winning it, or benefitted from prolonging the war, as it was a good excuse for establishing the rule of the regime emerging from the revolutionary chaos. The Iraqi side, on the other hand, seemed to want to end the war by any means, and so had resorted to tactics to scare ordinary people into forcing the Iranian regime to accept UN ceasefire resolutions. The Iraqis started what the media called the 'war of the cities,' bombing ordinary civilians.

The 'war of the cities' started for me as a high school junior one summer evening when my grandma, Maman Bahram, came downstairs announcing, "Saddam says he will be bombing the people of Tehran tomorrow."

"Good for him. How did you find out about it?" Mom asked, with a skeptical smirk. Until that point, the war had been restricted to military targets.

"Your aunt called me," she said. "It's on Radio Iraq. They're naming Tehran neighborhoods they will be destroying."

"Scare tactics," I opined. Somehow people were taking my opinion more seriously recently, and that had emboldened me to share it more often.

"Do you think so?" asked Maman Bahram. "Some folks are thinking of leaving town, you know."

"Oh yeah," I said, confidently. "He would never bomb residential areas in Tehran. Think of all the embassies and foreign business folks. Plus," I added, "Tehran is huge. The chance of a bomb landing in our neighborhood is slimmer than the chance of dying in a car crash."

At around two in the morning, we were awakened by the loud sound of two bombs going off, and my brother, Siamak, swore he'd heard the plane go by too. A few moments later, the sound of anti-aircraft started and went on for five minutes or so. I was hoping they would get the planes, but that they wouldn't crash into residential areas. It felt a bit scary but surely they had hit some military target and were heading back now. They couldn't be lingering too long, they'd run out of fuel. We turned on the TV but there was no mention of what was going on, and it had all gone silent and peaceful again, so everyone went back to bed.

When we got up the next morning, the phones didn't work. We didn't make much of it at first, but when my dad came back from the bakery with fresh bread, he said the bombs had actually landed only two blocks away from us, and that even VOA had mentioned our neighborhood by name. This was why the phones didn't work, because everyone was trying to call their friends and relatives in our area to check on them.

Siamak and I headed out to find out where the bombs had landed. All the windows had been broken. The main street had been closed to traffic, but a huge crowd surrounded the two buildings that had been leveled. People said two families had been killed in their sleep. The rescue workers were still digging. For some reason we'd been spared from the impact even though buildings beyond our house had their windows shattered. I checked the whole house when I got back and only found one broken lamp on the third floor in my uncle's suite.

That stage of the 'war of the cities' lasted two months or so, and none of the subsequent air raids were close to where we lived. The next stage started a year later, lasting for three or four months. That too, spared us.

The last stage of the bombings started in the winter of the next year, by which time I was a sophomore at Sharif. Leading up to it, there were no forewarnings or threats on Radio Iraq. The air raid was particularly loud and made us run up the stairs to the roof to see if we could locate the smoke cloud, but we didn't find anything.

Thirty minutes or so later, the phone rang.

"Babak!" called Mom, who'd answered it. "It's Nadia. She wants to talk to you."

Nadia was my uncle's wife. My uncle had been away on a business trip and she'd been by herself for the last week or so, taking care of her father and her one-month-old son.

"Hello?"

"Babak…" her voice was a bit faint and worried, and she talked quickly. "Listen to me carefully and please don't let anyone know because I don't want them to panic."

"OK…?"

"The bomb landed on our neighbor's house. We're all good and just got some minor scratches. We're at the hospital now. Go to our place. All the windows are broken and I want to make sure someone's there."

"Got it!"

I hung up and started putting my shoes on.

"What is it, Babak?"

"Nadia needs me to run an errand," I said quickly. "I'm taking Maman Bahram's car."

"Let's go," came the voice of my grandpa, Baba Javad. He had his cap and jacket on and seemed to know what my mission was about. My grandparents lived upstairs and we shared the phone with them. He must have been listening in on my conversation with Nadia.

Baba Javad sat silently next to me, with his hand on the dashboard, holding himself steady as I drove as fast as I could through the afternoon traffic, honking and waving at people to make way.

My uncle's place was on a steep road called Velenjak, which led to the Tochal Mountain recreation area. They had already set a roadblock at the entrance, but the revolutionary guard let us through after asking us for our destination address. They wouldn't let anyone through the second roadblock, halfway up Velenjak, though.

I parked the car on the curb.

"I'll see you there," I called to Baba Javad, and ran the six blocks up the mountain at my top speed.

The bombs had landed on my uncle's neighbor's house, across the street, and there was a crowd of onlookers and rescue workers around the wreckage. I didn't stop. I swung around and ran into the front yard of the apartment complex towards my uncle's house.

The front door was broken and half-open. As I pulled the knob, I noticed the door was covered with glass shards on the inside. I walked in, stepping on broken glass, taking in the devastation. The walls were covered with shards of glass sticking out like daggers. They had been blown out of the large windows across the hall, about forty feet away. There wasn't a single window that had not shattered.

How could they have survived this? I thought.

As I went around the hall, I noticed the wall nearest the bomb blast was standing at an angle and, looking up, I could see the darkening wintery sky through the large opening all along where the wall used to meet the ceiling.

There was blood on the floor near the kitchen doorway. I followed the trail of blood to one of the windows, where I found the baby cot upside down on the floor. I straightened it and was shocked to find it full of dark blood where the baby's head would have been.

Shoot! She must have lied to me.

My heart started pounding. I ran to the phone, but there was no dial tone. I noticed the blood trail was leading down the stairs and to the laundry room. The windows downstairs were all broken too.

"Babak!" Grandpa called from upstairs.

I ran back up the stairs. "There's a lot of blood," I said.

"Is the phone working?"

"No."

"They must have taken them to the university hospital down the road." He put his hat back on. "I'll go find them."

I kept walking around the house, checking every nook and cranny, trying to picture what might have happened immediately after the bombing. My brain was in overdrive, looking for a way to explain to myself that everything was OK, and distracting myself from the nauseating sensation in my stomach.

By the time the damage assessment folks showed up, the phone had been reconnected and I'd gotten some news on what had happened from home.

"Was anyone home during the raid?" the large man in the firefighter suit asked.

"Yes, a woman, an old man, and a one-month-old baby."

"Did anyone get hurt?" he asked as he took notes.

"The baby's OK. The old man has internal bleeding below his left ear, but he is conscious. My uncle's wife got twenty-seven stitches on her leg due to flying glass."

I got the full story later on from Nadia. She had been in the kitchen when she heard the plane and a whizzing sound. She was lucky to have walked out just in time to miss the flying shards of glass from the kitchen windows, but not too quickly, or she wouldn't have been shielded from the flying glass in the hall by the pillar across from the kitchen door. Still, she'd been hit by a shard that tore through her right leg.

Her father had been lying down for an afternoon nap. Had he stayed lying down, the glass would have flown over him, but he'd sat up and was knocked on the head by a flying stereo. He had gotten back up after the raid to check on my cousin in the baby cot. The blood in the cot was his. In a state of panic, the three of them had dragged themselves downstairs to the laundry room and hid there, even though the raid was over. The first responder emergency crew had found them there and loaded them in one of the ambulances.

I showed the tilting wall to the damage assessment guy. "This is the only structural damage I could find. Otherwise, there isn't a single window intact."

He took a business card out of his front pocket, wrote a number on it and handed it to me. "There will be a van on Velenjak tomorrow morning distributing supplies. Show this to them and get some plastic to cover the windows for the next few days. Call me if they don't show up for a full assessment in a couple of days. They'll pay you to fix the windows and that wall."

Nadia called that evening and asked me to stay at their place for the night, so I started clearing an area downstairs. There was glass everywhere, including on all the beds, blankets, and sheets. I found three small carpets in a wooden closet downstairs that had been spared. There were a couple of electric heaters too. I placed them side by side to heat my whole body as I lay on and under the carpets. It was uncomfortable and cold and hot at the same time, and the image of the bloody baby cot kept coming to my mind. I don't think I slept much that night.

***

Scud missiles were different and, in many ways, scarier. Saddam had tried bombing raids on civilians with no success and this, during the last two years of the war, represented an escalation. The air raid sirens would now go off one or two minutes before the massive explosion—people said they'd employed lookouts near the border to spot the incoming missiles—and in the sky above where the missile landed, a little white cloud of smoke would linger for a few minutes.

The missiles were huge; I saw an unexploded one being hauled away on a truck once. It must have been thirty feet long, at least. The devastation was also much larger than anything we'd experienced before. The casualty tolls we heard through word-of-mouth were now in the double digits each time. One of the early hits was on a supermarket on the side of a large square called *Haft-e-Tir* and it completely destroyed the whole thing. I heard of one hitting a kindergarten too. Many small children had died. Casualties, as usual, were never published.

My term started a few days into this period of the war, commonly, and somewhat poetically, called the rain-of-missiles. There had been some debate as to whether the university would be open, given the circumstances, but the newspapers announced that they would and that it was business as usual.

I had a class at seven in the morning and I'd left home shortly after an attack at five-thirty. When I got to the university, however, they would not let anyone in. The missile had landed on the campus, destroying a large part of the chemistry and metallurgy departments[1], and the university was shut down.

Uncle Kourosh had a tiny little apartment in a village near the Dizin ski resort, and so we headed there for safety, and more importantly, to maintain our sanity. The probability of being hit was low, but having to go through a missile attack once or twice a day can really wear you down, especially if you have nothing better to do than to wait for it to end.

Dizin is three hours north of Tehran, but that is due to the twisting mountain road you have to take to get there. If you draw a straight line to Dizin from Tehran, it's probably no more than fifteen miles away. Tehran cannot be seen from the slopes, but you know where it is from the smog. There was no smog when we were skiing in Dizin; many had left Tehran, like us, and the traffic was light.

Skiing in this context was rather surreal. Sometimes, the little cloud from the missile's point of turn above Tehran could be seen from the slopes. Everyone on the slopes would stop and look at it, probably wondering where it had landed and wishing minimum casualties but concluding that there was nothing they could do about it, turning around, and resuming their skiing.

Siamak and I had made friends with some of the locals and we'd get together with them at night to play cards. They would ask us questions about city life, and we'd ask them all we'd ever wanted to know about living in a mountain village.

"The donkeys here look so sad, it's depressing. Why are they so sad?" I asked one time.

"They're pretty happy before they're castrated," one of the local kids said, shuffling the cards for another round.

"How do they do that?"

"What?"

"You know, castrate them."

"Oh." He smiled at me. "You really wanna know?"

"Yeah."

"They take two bricks..." He held his hands open in front of him.

---

1 This proved to be quite a blessing: when the campus eventually reopened, and while those two departments were still being reconstructed, their students were stationed at the computer department, and we realized how girl-rich those departments had been.

"And…" He clapped his hands together loudly and laughed, making us all grimace and feeling a twinkle in our testicles.

***

The university partly reopened for the next term but, as a safety precaution, the classes were held on the first floor of the twenty-floor-high Hilton hotel. As with most safety precautions, this too came too late, and the rain-of-missiles ended shortly after they announced the move to the hotel. There was very little in the way of administrative services that term, so I couldn't fix the zeroes on my report card, and by the term after that, I'd been picked for the student military draft and had to skip school for six months and serve in the air force.

Amazingly, with the bombings and missiles and the war being temporary interruptions, life seemed to quickly bounce back to the normal and mundane.

At the end of my last term at the university, I was given a form to take to the professors teaching courses for which I had zeroes on my report card. The last form I needed filled was for professor Yassai. I found him in his office and explained what I needed.

"When did you have the course with me sir?" he asked me, in his usual monotone.

"1367, sir. Fall term."

"Let me check," he said, opening the top drawer of a filing cabinet. He briefly opened one of the files and put it back, closing the drawer. "Not there." Then he opened the top left-hand drawer of his desk and opened one of the files in it and put it back almost immediately.

"Not there either." He turned to me. "I'm sorry, but as a matter of policy, we do not keep records of grades for more than two years."

I stood there looking at him blankly for a moment.

"But sir, I have a zero on my report card and I won't be able to graduate unless I get my grade for stats corrected."

"Oh dear!" he said and proceeded to check the same two files in the same two drawers again. "Not there either. I'm sorry, but as a matter of policy, we do not keep records of grades for more than two years."

"I got a 12.5."

"Yes," he said, ambiguously.

"Would you please fill out the form then?"

"Oh dear!" he said and went through the searching routine once more.

"Maybe they are in a different file?" I asked.

"No, no! Can't be," he said. "I'm sorry, but as a matter of policy—"

"I understand that, sir, but with all due respect, what am I to do about my grade?"

"You will have to retake stats 101, sir."

This was ridiculous and I was losing my patience. "Can you just please trust me and fill the form? Why would I lie about my grade? 12.5 isn't anything to brag about."

"Oh dear!" He walked towards the top drawer again. I left, cursing my luck, contemplating jumping off the Ebnesina building. Everyone laughed at Yassai's antics but when it came to me, his crazy had turned out to be a complete pain in the rear.

Down the stairs, I noticed the door to the dean of the math department's office was open and he was at his desk. Normally you'd have to make an appointment and go through his admin, but this was too inviting not to try.

"May I take a quick moment of your time, sir?" I asked as I approached him. "I need this form filled but apparently there's no record of my grade anymore."

He gestured to me to hand him the form.

"Why do you need the grade?"

"Our department changed the pre-requisites several times since we started and I ended up with zeroes in my grade card for some of the courses, sir."

"What's your score?"

"12.5, sir. The professor says I need to take the course all over again."

He looked at me with a smile. "Yassai?"

I nodded.

He jotted down some notes on a sticky paper. "Leave the form with me and pick it up tomorrow."

***

The dean's office was quite busy the next day, but when I mentioned why I was there, his admin fetched me the form. It was all filled out and signed, and my shiny grade of 12.5 was entered in. There were also three double-sided handwritten pages attached to it. The whole thing was one long rambling sentence by Yassai, about how this honest-looking student had approached him for this form and how it had been his policy to discard grades after two years, and how the respected dean of the department had requested him to make an exception in this particular case and to trust the honest-looking student and fill out the form in spite of the fact that he would have strongly advised against it, recommending instead for the honest-looking student to take the course again, as the chances for him to achieve a higher score would also increase, given the distribution of student grades in recent terms...

At the administrative office, I handed the form to the person in charge of report cards.

"What's this?" he asked, looking at the attachment. But before I could explain anything, he tore it off and crumbled it in his hand. "Yassai!" He tossed the crumbled letter into the trash bin next to his desk. "That guy's crazy."

BOOT CAMP

*T*owards the end of the Iran-Iraq War, in spring of 1988, the Iranian army faced a shortage of recruits and, for a brief period of time, instituted a student draft. University juniors were drafted at random to serve a six-month term at the fronts. Most of us had drawn our biggest motivation to study and enter universities from the fact that students were 'fighting at the education front' and were excluded from the draft, so this was not welcome news at all.

The first batch of student-draftees was sent to the fronts at the tail end of the war, when the fighting was especially fierce. I had heard horror stories about deaths and injuries amongst the students, none of whom I knew personally. My name came out for the second student draft, days after the war was over. My brother, Siamak, kept accusing me of being lucky, but I guess being lucky depends on the context—the student draft was abolished immediately after I served in the second batch.

We were randomly seeded and I was, again, lucky enough to stay in Tehran and to be placed in the air force, better known amongst the draftees as Hotel Homa. The drill instructors were quite lenient with us, well aware of the fact that, as university students, we were completely misplaced in the boot camp.

The officer in charge of our group, Captain Sai-si, was a handsome, clean-shaven fellow, who did everything in style. His military salute was a study in cool: he would hold his palm up and steady it slightly away from his forehead and then lean into it with a twinkle in his eyes and a face that seemed to be on the verge of a smile. He was hard to read for us. That may have been intentional on his side, or maybe it was just the way he was. We respected him immensely, and, over the course of the boot camp, we went from fearing him and the strict, seemingly inhumane rules of the military, to accepting his absolute authority over us and wanting to always please him.

As for me, my whole tact was to blend in and not be seen. I didn't want to be known as a troublemaker, nor did I want everyone to think I was going out of my way to endear myself to our commanders. I was constantly looking for, and trying to be, the median. This, I felt, was the safest approach to survive boot camp.

They would give us our weekly schedule every Saturday. One time, upon seeing 'obstacle course' in the schedule, we prepared ourselves for a day of hard physical labor, but Captain Sai-si basically gave us a tour of the obstacle course, describing what each section was for, and telling us stories about people who'd either completed the course in exceptional time, or had miserably failed. We then found a spot in the shade and sat around telling jokes for the rest of the day.

Our 'night raids' were sort of similar: we were given ample forewarning, and enough time to dress up and board the bus to the shooting range. Captain Sai-si would buy watermelon and sunflower seeds on the way there, which we'd consume after a light, nightly hike in the hills.

"The key," he kept saying, "is we should be quiet, and there should be no lights."

I'm not sure who we were hiding from, the make-believe enemy, or the other drill instructors who might tell on our captain for not giving us a hard time.

On the last week of boot camp, the schedule called for a 'night raid' on Wednesday, and many of us had a problem with that: Wednesday night was *Oshin* night. We had a TV in our group's mess room and, even though the lights went off at ten p.m., we were allowed to watch TV there after the curfew.

Oshin was a very popular Japanese TV series about an entrepreneur of humble beginnings, born in an orphanage, brought up by her grandfather, but ultimately opening a large department store in Tokyo. It was heavily censored and the story was changed through dubbing and creative re-editing—for instance, I found out later that she'd actually worked at a brothel for a while and the old lady who kept bossing her around was really not her great aunt, or that her favorite drink was sake, not grape juice. But at the time, it was universally watched and talked about in Iran.

"Maybe if we're on our best behavior, the captain would get us back in time," one of the guys suggested.

"Oshin's grandpa is sick. How could we miss tonight's episode?"

"There's no way we'd make it. We usually leave at nine and we've never gotten back before midnight."

But Captain Sai-si did show up early that evening and we were ready and lined up for him faster than ever. He had us march to the gun storage facility to pick up our standard issue machineguns. We were very organized and followed his instructions carefully. On the bus, we pleaded with him not to stop for food.

"Let's skip the watermelon, Captain."

He ignored us, but didn't stop the bus either.

When we got to the shooting range, we got out of the bus and lined up, self-organizing and requiring very little supervision. We were as quiet as we could be. We just couldn't afford to wait for a speech or a group punishment—"In the military, we reward the individual but punish the group."

The night march was a very quiet affair during which even the captain didn't say much, not even bothering to repeat his stories about how important it was to be silent or how a cigarette light could be seen from ten kilometers away.

After twenty minutes or so, he sat us down atop one of the hills. He looked at his watch and gazed out at the dark horizon a couple of times.

"You guys have gotten better," he said, still staring at the horizon. "Much better."

"Thank-you–sir," we said, in whispered military unison.

"Yeah... what time is it, Gharavi?" he asked.

"Ten past nine, sir."

"Yeah... you are much better organized. I commend you for this." He looked at us a bit more, still hesitant, and finally said, "OK, enough of this. Let's go back. 'ten-tion!"

We all jumped to our feet immediately and followed his instructions back to the bus.

"Can you get us back by nine-thirty?" the captain asked the driver softly, once we were all seated.

The driver gave him a smile. "I'll do my best, sir."

And his best was pretty scary good. He maneuvered the large vehicle around traffic and through yellow lights at an impressive speed. It was like a roller coaster ride, with the bus leaning heavily to each side on the turns. In spite of that though, when we got to the boot camp it was nine-forty, and we still had to return the guns.

The captain marched us to the gun storage, but the officer wasn't there. He must have expected us later and was probably at dinner or something. We stood there, in formation, for fifteen minutes, until he was tracked down. Organized as we were, it took our group of fifty or so students another five minutes to return the guns. It was getting late.

"OK, I'll skip the headcount," Captain Sai-si said. "Is everybody here?"

"Yes-sir!"

"Forward-MARCH!"

We started marching, but our dorm was on the other side of the camp. There was no way we'd get there on time.

"Give us the double-march, sir," a few of us said.

The double-march was simply a fast model of the march; we were to remain in formation and in step with the group.

The captain smiled. "OK… double-MARCH!"

No sooner had the words left his mouth than the first two rows of the group started sprinting towards the dorms.

"Stop! Stop!" the captain called. We stopped but the sprinters were already halfway across the yard.

The captain ran after them, furious, cursing under his breath, as we stood there, not quite knowing what to do.

"The idiots!" someone said after a long silence.

"To think that we put in so much effort to be good tonight," said someone else.

"What's gonna happen to them?" Gharavi asked.

"Punishment is for the group, remember? He's gonna take it out on all of us," said a slim guy with a permanently scared face, wide-eyed.

"Should we just stay here?"

"Yeah, let's not make it any worse than it is," the slim guy said.

A few minutes later, the captain came back to fetch us. He was frowning and looked angrier than we'd ever seen him. He gave us orders to march but didn't say anything else.

I was scared. What was he going to do? All those threats about sending insubordinate soldiers to jail and ambiguous references to 'ultimate disciplinary measures' started ringing in my ear. He could easily nullify our whole boot camp and have us take it all over again. It was within his power. Running around like that in the boot camp during curfew was not a negligible sin, and we all knew that. The captain's job was on the line, should the military police find out.

We soon found out what had happened to the guys in the first two rows. As we got closer to the dorms, we first heard a scraping noise, and soon could make out the figures of our comrades, flat on their chests, crawling across the yard. The captain stood us in attention and went to attend to them.

It wasn't fun to watch, and the dark made us imagine the worst. He seemed to be kicking those who were not doing the move correctly, and sometimes beating them for seemingly no good reason other than to inflict pain. His voice was not angry, and he restricted himself to short commands.

"Keep the heels…" *thump*, "down!"

"Hands…" *whip*, "forward!"

"Faster!" *Slap*.

After a few minutes he lined them up and gave them the squatting order. They started counting, "One, two, …"

He had them squat a good twenty times before he gave them the pigeon walk. This entailed squatting down and jumping forward while holding one's hands behind one's head. He made them go the length of the yard, and whoever fell behind was given push-ups.

Finally, he had them join us and stand in attention. He walked to the front of the group and looked us over. He was frowning and there was no trace of the usual smile on his face.

What is he thinking? Is the group punishment part of the process coming up?

"You will remain in attention," he said softly, and he left us and entered our dorm.

No one dared move, let alone speak. Was this an inspection of our beds and closets? They had made us redo our beds and clean up the dorm for hours in the first few days. It was a lesson in cleanliness and humility. Somehow, though, I thought of that as being too light a punishment for what had transpired. So, what was he up to?

Let's just get it over with, for crying out loud!

Moments later we all got our answer. The light in the mess room came on, along with sounds that could only have been coming from the TV set.

It took me a while to realize what was happening. The captain was sitting in our mess room, watching *Oshin*, while we were lined up in the dark outside, standing in attention. We did not dare move. For all we knew, he was checking on us from the second-floor window.

Standing in attention is not easy. After a few minutes, your ankles start hurting and your calves begin to burn. The neck and lower back come next. Your head and various unreachable parts of your body start itching, and you start having little dizzy spells.

No one made a noise or said a word. I tried distracting myself by listening to the sounds from the TV set, but I couldn't quite make out the voices. Plus, I was a rare exception in that I did not follow the series as religiously and had missed the past few episodes, so I had very little context.

Fortunately, the captain had gotten to the show when it was halfway through, so we didn't have to stand there for the full hour. Once the credits music started, he turned the TV off, and his figure soon showed up through the entrance, walking slowly, squinting a bit, and still not smiling.

I was exhausted and aching and wondering how much longer he would keep us standing in attention, now that he was back to disciplining us.

He walked around us a bit, gazing at us with what seemed to be a look of curiosity, as if to ask, how could you guys have been so dumb? I could sense a speech coming, and sure enough, once he made his way to the front of the group, he stood on the curb around the yard and, in a soft, monotonic voice, began to speak.

"Tonight, you disappointed me," he said. "You disappointed me as your commander. You disappointed the air force for trusting you to be able to defend our beloved country. You disappointed your country for putting so much hope in you as its future. You disappointed your families. They expected more. Most importantly…" he paused. "You disappointed yourselves. You are better than this. You know you are better than this. You are the cream of the crop. You are the smartest of Iran's children. You will build the future for the country your fellow countrymen died to defend. Is this why they gave their lives?" He pointed at the vicinity of the place where we had committed our crime.

"*Is* it?"

We knew to be quiet. His speech had touched us, and it made us feel ashamed. He was right. We were a disappointment. I had a big lump in my throat and I felt I had let down everyone and everything I loved.

He stood there silently, looking us over and letting his words sink in.

"At... EASE!" he commanded, and the guilty group gave him a perfect at-ease by clasping our hands behind our backs and stomping our right feet apart in such unison it made a single loud thump with zero reverb.

"I will let you off this time," he said, to our collective relief. "This is the one chance you will get from me. Any minor waiver would mean failing boot camp. Do you understand that?"

"YES-SIR!"

"I want you to think about what happened tonight, and repent. You will have to work hard to redeem yourselves. Are you up to the hard work ahead of you?"

"YES-SIR!"

"Very well then." A smile suddenly broke out on his face. "One more thing," he said, and paused, then continued, sadly. "Tonight, Oshin's grandpa passed away."

THE TRIP

I was behind the wheel most of the way. I got very tired towards the end, and Dad took over near Boroujerd. I got back into the driver's seat in Andimeshk, though. Not sure why, but I wanted to be driving when we got to the city. I guess it's like climbing: in spite of the fatigue, when you get close to the peak, you want to be the one ahead of the group.

Dad was sitting beside me up front, and Mom, my brother Siamak, and my sister Sara were in the back. We were heading back to Ahwaz, the city of our childhood, two years after the end of the war, ten years since I had last been there. This was a destination remote not just by miles, but by time. A destination I had fled as a teen, and was visiting now as a college senior.

The road was busy. I drove ahead of Masoud's car for a while. But I couldn't see anything, only the night markers on the center divider. I couldn't tell the distance from the oncoming traffic. Many of the cars coming towards me had their headlights on and it hurt my eyes. Before sunset, I had noticed my reddened right eye in the mirror. It was burning now, probably the dust in the air. The road was well paved and surrounded by large, green fields.

Ahwaz, five kilometers. I made way for Masoud to take over. It was hard to pass cars on this road. Darn Masoud was driving really fast. Every time he took a car over, I had to drive at least a hundred and forty just to get to him. Siamak and Sara, who'd been working up a racket up until just now, had quieted down. Everyone was tired.

We'd planned to cut the trip in half by staying the night in Khoramabad, but Dr. Kaameli, Masoud's dad, had dissuaded us. "We'd have to take all the stuff out of the car, and we wouldn't make it in time for New Year, either."

He was right, but logic was no cure for exhaustion.

Mom said, "Look Sara, these are the fires."

"She's asleep," I said, having checked in the mirror just now.

"Where?" Sara was awake. Maybe she hadn't been sleeping in the first place.

Masoud turned.

"Dad, Masoud just turned."

"What? Oh! Yes. He's going through Kian Pars. Follow him. Just go straight and Kian Pars is at the light."

What a green town! Wide streets, with flowers everywhere, and tall trees. And palms.

"What's this, Dad? Wasn't this the international bookstore?"

"No, son. This is Kian Pars' second square."

"Oh." I was disappointed with myself. I thought I knew the place.

Dad gave me directions. Of course, I could see Masoud too. He was a couple of cars ahead. The Paykan, with three brake lights, and a red glow-in-the-dark strip on its fender. That was all I saw.

"Do we cross the bridge?"

"Yup. We're going to the club."

"The university is across the bridge too, right?"

"No, it's on this side… and that's the university's triangular building, right there."

"We went to see a few concerts here." I pointed.

"Yeah, remember?" Mom said. "Pari Zangeneh came to town once."

"You took me too," I said, proudly.

"I wanted to see her beautiful eyes but she had large dark sunglasses on." Pari Zangeneh, the famous opera singer before the revolution, had lost her eyes in a car crash. I wondered where she was now. Obviously, banned from singing.

"Turn here. This is the new bridge."

Siamak, who'd been quiet up until now, suddenly said, "Karoun! This is Karoun!"

Karoun was very large. It was huge. I'd never paid too much attention to this river. It had always just been there, and we'd always just crossed over it in our car.

"It's so big… It's huge, isn't it?"

"Turn here. This is the twenty-four-meter avenue."

"Twenty-four-meter…" Such a familiar name, but I didn't remember it at all.

Names and places were disjointed. My mind was a jumble of names and memories. I must have been here before. Those arches, those shaded sidewalks, I was a kid back then. What would a twelve-year-old remember of a city he'd only visited on shopping expeditions with his dad? I had to remember more. Surely there was more…

"Twenty-four-meter… that name's familiar."

***

"Done unloading our car, helping with Masoud's now," I announced.

"OK, let me load you then," Sia said, mischievously.

"Whaa..?" I objected. "You loaded me fifty times! I'll load you now." I gave him my evil smile. "Heh-heh-heh…!" I raised my eyebrows a few times. Sia laughed.

"Take this, and this, and I'll hang this one around your neck. Wait, there's more…"

Masoud came and we locked up the cars and took the rest of the stuff in.

"Wow! So, this is Ahwaz!"

I looked up at the sky. "Not that many stars. Must be pollution here too."

"Not pollution," Masoud corrected me, "this is because of the fires, remember?"

"Ah, yes. Look there. That orange color must be from the fires."

It was so green here. It was humid, but not as disturbingly humid as the Caspian shore - Shomal. Of course, March was a good time to visit Ahwaz.

Masoud always knew more than I. I was two months older, but, even now that we were both students, I asked him more about medicine than he asked me about computers.

"Mmm…" I took in a deep breath. "It smells so like Ahwaz here. I remember this smell. And that's the club building. I bet the Konar tree is still in front of it. It's Konar season now, isn't it?"

I guess I was talking too much. Masoud was quiet.

The building's front yard was covered in overgrown grass and weed. The walkway was a zigzag of paved squares. Walking on them was a bit tedious.

"Maybe we should have started with our left leg first," Masoud joked.

"Not practical. The stride's too big."

The building had a set of suites reserved for the university faculty. There was the Kooy too, but that was in high demand. The ceilings here were pretty high, maybe to keep it cool. There was a lamp burning atop the main entrance, with a cloud of mosquitos and insects surrounding it. Reminded me of Shomal again.

We heaved the door open with some difficulty and stepped inside. We could hear the kids making noise at the end of the hallway. Sara and Masoud's sister, Mariam. The Kaamelis were supposed to stay in the other building, but Dad had gotten the keys to five of the suites and so we were all staying together now.

All the fluorescent lights were on. People weren't saving on power here, it seemed. Next to one of the lights, I spotted a tiny lizard on the wall.

"Look there." I pointed.

"Yeah." Masoud saw it too.

"Crocodile?" I joked.

Masoud and I picked one of the suites. Sia and Kaivan, Masoud's little brother, picked another. The grown-ups had one each. We would use Dr. Mohebbi's suite for its restroom. That was the only Western-style toilet. For Sara, who couldn't use the Iranian-style ones due to her cerebral palsy.

My sister Sara was one when we fled Ahwaz. She had been diagnosed with cerebral palsy the next year, the same year everything bad seemed to have unfolded at the same time. She used crutches and was constantly in physiotherapy.

Masoud lay on the bed. I took my towel and clothes out of my bag.

"You're gonna take a shower?" Masoud asked.

"Yeah. Clean up, then we need to go to the TV room for the moment of the New Year Tahvil."

"Really? Aren't you tired?" he asked, and I noticed his bloodshot eyes.

"You're going to sleep?" I needed him to help me stay up.

"I'm really tired."

"Lazy bum! You can't sleep through Tahvil!" I switched to my mock voice. "Start of the year, one thousand, three hundred and sixty-nine."

"Hmm…" He shut his eyes.

I got a bar of soup and a sponge from Mom and took a quick shower. The water was nice and warm. Everyone was cleaning up.

I was thinking that when I got back to Tehran, I could write down my memories of this trip. Then I thought, *Nah, it's just gonna end up as another one of those projects that are easier to start than finish.*

Masoud took a shower too. We put on our nice clothes and headed to the TV room.

I got on a call with Tehran, like the others. This was the same payphone Dad had always been using to call Tehran. The other professors, too. The sound of them dropping coins to continue the call, like the tick-tock of a wall clock, always reminded me to hurry. The voice from the other side was so faint. The usual greetings and niceties with grandparents and uncles.

We all gathered around the TV set. It was midnight. We needed to wait another fifty minutes for the Tahvil or Vernal Equinox, the moment all Iranians around the world celebrate the coming of spring and the New Year.

As usual, the shows were crappy. Boring and unfunny. I tried to get Basra or Kuwait TV, but I failed. The humidity was probably not right.

Dr. Kaameli was really sleepy. "You guys stick around for the New Year. I'm going to bed."

We all smiled at him. "Goodnight."

Kaivan left too. Our numbers were dwindling. Sara and Mariam followed suit.

"There's nothing on TV, dears," Mom said. "Why don't you guys go to bed and get your presents tomorrow morning?"

I suggested we go for a walk with Masoud. I didn't want him to retire early. I needed some way to stay awake too.

"This is Moord, you know," Masoud said, pointing at the bushes surrounding the yard like a wall.

I was surprised. "This? But the leaves… This is so different. This is Moord? Can't be."

"Yeah, don't you remember?"

"Yeah… but…" I noticed the Konar tree. "Let's go there."

A huge flock of birds started chirping violently as soon as we got close.

"Did we wake them up?" Masoud was clearly still fantasizing about his bed.

There were tall fences across the long, grassy yard.

"That's the swimming pool, isn't it?" I asked.

Masoud nodded. The fence was new. We headed towards it. Another flock of birds noisily flew out of another tree near the pool. It was dark. And scary.

"Never mind," Masoud said.

We turned back. We were standing in front of a large building now. I could see a huge mirror standing inside.

"Stop peeping!" Masoud pushed me. "People live here."

"Did you see that mirror?"

"This used to be the residence of the British Consul."

"Really? What was he doing here?"

"The whole place used to be the British Consulate. That's why it looks so nice. The embassy gifted it to the university, and they turned it into the faculty club."

We were back outside the TV room. I looked inside.

"Masoud, everyone's gone to bed." It was twelve-thirty.

"Let's go sleep, man." Masoud turned towards the suites.

I was not sleepy. I was exhausted, though. Couldn't help it.

When in bed, I turned on the radio to try to stay awake for the New Year. Someone was making a speech. Then someone else came on reading some stupid prose in praise of spring. I turned the radio off and went to sleep.

No one stayed awake for the New Year.

***

Saturday. The gatekeeper said they changed the water on Saturdays and that he'd just turned the tap on. We were here with my dad. We changed into our swimsuits and went in. The weather was hot, but the water was ice cold. I was in the deep end. The water hadn't reached the shallow side yet. We splashed around. Dad was a great play friend. We were lying on the grass now, all tired out. Dad was reading a book and I was climbing the Konar tree. This place was much better when it was crowded.

The pool had a unique shape. It was like… like nothing. No angles, like a few adjacent circles. There was a shelf all around the periphery that was always full of frogs. I didn't like it at first, but now, they were just part of the pool.

***

Masoud said, "Let's swim the width."

I knew how to swim, but a full width! I wasn't sure. If Masoud was going, I had to go. The girls were here too. Mothers, fathers. Mrs. Ehdai was taking a sun bath. She was always taking sun baths. I'd never seen her swim. Mr. Soleimani was lying on the grass reading a book.

Masoud gave a speech here once. It was our fifth-grade graduation ceremony. He kept breaking his Persian speech with American style 'ums' that became the butt of jokes for some time afterwards. "We the students of… um…. The Center for… um… Pre-university Education… um…"

***

We were here for lunch with Professor Eastop, a visiting scholar from the British Museum. I don't remember us having ever had anything but Chelokabab at the club restaurant. It was Chelokabab again this time. Professor Eastop was trying to learn Farsi. He took out his notebook. His hair was all grey, and he had a goatee. His face and hands were pale white, but he was handsome. Blue-eyed.

"OK, on to education now," he said in his BBC accent. "What is Salad in Farsi?"

"Salad," Mom replied, with a smile.

He thought about it a bit and wrote it down in his notebook.

"What's Soup in Farsi?"

We laughed out loud. Soup in Farsi is Soup, of course. He wrote it into his notebook anyway. He had a habit of holding his notebook half-open, up to his face while writing into it.

Halfway through lunch he turned to me and said, "There is only one other person I know in the world that has worse eating manners than you."

I wasn't sure what he meant by 'eating manners,' but I had noticed how stiff and elaborate he had been all during lunch.

"Who?" I asked.

"My own son!"

We all laughed, but I was a bit annoyed for the rest of the meal, not knowing how to eat to avoid becoming the worst.

***

I saw Masoud's teacher, a little old lady with curly hair. She looked just like Agatha Christie. She taught the English-speaking students. Their lessons were much more interesting. Just like playing games. Masoud said she'd seen half the world. My English wasn't bad, but Dad wanted me to take regular Persian speaking classes.

I said hello and she replied. Dad introduced himself to her. She asked us why we were there. We said we came to swim in the pool, but that they were changing the water, and we'd been playing in the half-full pool anyway.

"Oh, how delightful it must have been. But you must be careful, you know. You might catch a tummy ache."

***

When you pick an apple, it should be hard and yellow, or green. But for Konar, it's the opposite. Too hard, and your mouth will suffer from the worst bitter aftertaste ever, and no Konar tastes good after that. Pick the ripe ones, the softer and squishier the better. Hand the harder ones to Mom so she puts them on top of the fridge to ripen in a day or two.

***

We woke up at ten, Masoud before me; we had breakfast and went outside. Sia and Kaivan found one of the Arab workers from the other building and borrowed a pump from them to inflate the basketball. Sara and Mariam showed up too.

"Who is this man? Masood? Masood! Who is this man?" Mariam kept asking, being her usual persistent three-year-old self.

The air smelled really like the Ahwaz I remembered. And it was so green everywhere. And clean. You could see the smoke from the fires in the horizon, but the sky was still very blue.

Masoud suddenly noticed Mariam.
She was singing,

Amaleh dasteh dasteh,
Kenareh joo neshasteh,
(The workers gathered in bunches
By the sewage, eat their lunches…)

Masoud jumped in alarm. "Mariam! Keep quiet! Mariam!"
"What?"
"Just…" Clearly Mariam was too young to know she might be offending the workers if she sang the next two verses.

Sigaaria be doresh
Jam mishan dasta dasta
Digeh nemrom velaayat amalamo nemiom velayat.
(Puffing on cheap cigarettes
Making circles with smoke jets
Back to our farms? We'll never go!
Rather be poor, but return? No!)

"Just go to the playground and play with Sara," Masoud said.
I crossed the plastic soccer ball a few times. Kaivan brought the basketball. We headed to the playground.
"This was here?"
Masoud nodded.
Looked like I'd never noticed these grounds before, especially this tennis court.

***

"Should we go inside?"
We were trying to peek through the large windows of what used to be the club restaurant.
"But it's closed."
"The door is open though."
We went around the back. Not much in there to see. The only thing

memorable about the restaurant was the Chelokabab anyway.

No one else seemed to be in the entire gated club area. It was like they'd kept everyone out. We went to the wall around the swimming pool and found a crack to see through.

"So small!"

"I wish we could get to it."

We went around, and sure enough, the gates were wide open.

"So, this was the pool then…"

It was empty. Neglected and dirty, full of cracks. The shallow part looked really shallow. The whole thing had shrunk considerably. I jumped inside. "Come on!"

Masoud showed the deep part. "Look! It's not even my height. Remember how deep it used to be?"

We stood in the deep end. Of course, it wasn't my height. Must have been three meters or so.

Masoud smiled awkwardly. "Well, almost." Then he continued, more seriously. "Remember how swimming a width was such a feat for us?"

We climbed out.

"The Karoun River is behind this wall, isn't it?"

"Yeah."

"Let's go."

We got to a fence, "Let's go there."

"The door's shut."

"We can go over it. Look." I jumped over to the other side. Everyone else followed. A few Arabs were standing near the riverbank. There was a two- or three-meter drop to the water. There was another fence. We threw a few stones.

"It's like the sea."

"The water is brown."

"It's washing the whole of Iran out," Masoud said.

I pointed with mock excitement, "Look! There's a piece of the Shahyad monument!"

We laughed and started walking towards the bridge.

"Look at that guy." Kaivan pointed. "So brave!"

Someone was walking on the big arch on the old hanging bridge. It was very high.

"Jump! You can do it! Jump!" I called, knowing he was too far away to hear me.

There was another man walking up the other arch too.

"What if one of them falls?" Sia asked.

"They wouldn't be up there if they didn't know what they were doing now, would they?" Masoud said.

"Well, how do they know they wouldn't fall?" Sia wouldn't let go.

"It's a chicken and egg thing," Kaivan said.

"No, it's not," Masoud said, definitively, settling the argument.

We were near the bridge now. There were a few horses in a distance. Looked like they were giving rides.

"Look!" I pointed. "There are boats for hire over there."

"Wanna go on one?" Masoud asked enthusiastically.

"Let's go."

"Let's do it later," Siamak said. "I don't feel like it."

I gave him an angry stare that seemed to persuade him to change his mind.

"How do we get down there?"

After overcoming a few more obstacles, we were riding on a boat on the Karoun. Twenty tomans each. The price of a pack of gums.

"There are sharks in the Karoun, you know."

I was deep in thought. Not bad. Where else in the world could you do this? In other places in the world people my age had girlfriends and were starting to get serious...

Why is it that every time I start thinking about 'where else in the world,' I'm actually thinking about America? I'm sure there are plenty of places in the world that have it worse than us.

I hope not. They say there's always a worse. Some place in the world will have to be the worst for spending your youth. I guess it all depends on one's self. It's all relative anyway. Relative to everywhere else, this is the worst.

After resolving this debate in my head, I became aware of my surroundings again. A few seagulls, and every once in a while, one of them dove into the water, but not to hunt. Just to make us look! We were getting close to the floating bridge. It wobbled on the waves with every car passing by.

Every day I was after a nearer goal, like writing a book that was forever in need of a narrative. My goal right now was to go to the Kooy. I wanted to find out what it looked like after all these years. *My happy childhood.* When I lived there, I never got a chance to compare it to anything else.

That's why it was only after I left that I realized how good it was. A big family. A big home with a big backyard. Huge. All my friends and their families lived in it. I was never aware of any ugliness in that society. The ugliness I was part of now. It was like being away from your family for ten years. It wasn't that important that your family had also changed during the same time. You just wanted to get back. Maybe it would be better.

***

We had our own problems back then: Lilly Shirzadeh, the neighborhood tomboy, with Amir Attari—both a year older than me, and stronger—ganging up to shove Moord down my clothes. The area maintenance crew were cutting the shrubs we called Moord and the branches and leaves lay everywhere. This had inspired the neighborhood bullies' latest mischief.

I kept shouting, "Do it! Do it! I'll show you... Aw! I'll tell my mom!"

Then, much more enthusiastically than I expected, they came to our door with me.

"Mom! These guys shoved Moord down my clothes!"

"Why did you shove Moord down his clothes, guys?" Mom asked them.

"But Ma'am, he keeps telling us to do it."

Mom turned to me. "If you told them to do it then what are you complaining about?"

Very disappointing. The door shut on my face. Lilly and Amir left. I stared at the door for a while, shrugged it off, and ran out to play again. Football, kickball, or maybe hide-and-seek.

I ran into Lilly in Amir Abad, two years after the war started. Dad was walking us to school. She had a veil and manteau on. A slight lipstick. Some of her hair was showing, and she was wearing perfume. She was walking towards us with a bunch of other girls.

"Oh! Hi, Lilly, how are you?"

"Hi Babak, how are you?"

She stood in front of me for a short moment. We looked at one another. I had nothing to say. Maybe it was the same for her. She was a lady now and didn't look like she'd want to be Super Boy anymore when we played superheroes.

I walked on. And so did she. *We will never see each other again.*

I was a different person now, as ugly and cruel as the world I was living in. It was easy for me now to just say hi and walk away from an old friend and suppress the urge to turn around and talk to her, because that is what a young man with dignity does. This was what being grown-up meant: suppress your childish carefree impulsiveness and act like a dignified adult.

Dad had said, "Son, society has an ugly side to it that you will have to learn. You will have to get in with it. You will have to learn to take responsibility. It is not all about you anymore."

I will have to become a liar and develop some sort of a mental complex. Just like my society. Maybe they don't even know it themselves, or even if they do, they don't care. They didn't grow up in the Kooy. They have no relative point of comparison. I still remember what was good.

I'd been so deep in self-flatulating thoughts, I'd completely forgotten where and when I was. The boat was edging next to the pier and I don't remember enjoying any of the Karoun scenery. My eyes had been looking inward the whole while.

Somehow, the boat ride on the Karoun made me angry. We got off and walked back.

***

We were heading back to the Kooy for the first time after ten years. Heading back to see where we used to live before fleeing the war.

Dr. Kaameli's car was in front of us. He had the campus badge and they let him in. We followed. The street was lined with tall palms and Nerium. The buildings were hidden behind the trees. It wasn't like this before.

Dad explained for Sara. "Look, dear, this used to be the sports complex. We came here to see Chamran a few days after the war started. We signed up for the Basij para-military group. We thought it was the patriotic thing to do now that the war was raging so close to home. Just then a missile hit next to the Olympic-size pool and we all took cover under the table. Chamran didn't even blink. He said we should all go for now and that he'd call us if he needed us. I guess it was obvious we weren't soldier material."

He'd told us the story many times, but this time it had visual accompaniment.

We passed the agriculture department and parking lot. I remembered it well. Of course, it used to be a bit larger.

"The sports complex is still under the Basij. Not even the dean has been able to take it back. They must have totally destroyed the facilities."

We passed the soccer field. When I was six, I saw a cow up close for the first time here. I'd walked up to it cautiously with Dad's encouragement. I'd even touched its side. It was regurgitating in a state of extreme cool and indifference. She had been a picture of dignity.

"Oh! Looks like they finally reclaimed the soccer field. They've taken down the walls."

"Was it taken by the Basij too?" Siamak asked.

"Yeah. Up until recently. Looks like they took it back though."

"This leads to the hospital, that way," Mom said, pointing. "Sara-jaan, that's where we first met you."

"Let's go there, Mom. Can we go see?"

Everyone disagreed. "What for?" "No, dear, there's nothing to see." "Nothing there."

We were at the gates of the Kooy now. This was the Kooy's store. Berenji.

***

We used to complain about his high prices. Thinking back, I don't think his prices were particularly high. It was fashionable to complain about retailers for prices. I used to secretly buy Cheetos from him. One time we went there with the other kids to buy soda and I pulled out a hundred-toman bill.

"Wow!"

"*Wolek*, look at that!"

"He's rich!"

I couldn't quite tell if they were making fun of me or if it was genuine surprise.

***

The main street and the houses. How small! I was feeling dizzy. The houses had shrunk. The street was so short. The bricks were tiny. All houses had brick facades. We were already at the end of the street! We even passed a few rows of houses that were new since we had left. So small. Like matchboxes. Masoud's car stopped. I grabbed my camera and jumped out.

Dr. Kaameli was greeting some folks, and we dashed off.

170

The school. So small.

"The trees have grown so large. The eucalyptuses look ancient."

"Where's the school's playground roof?"

"Don't you know?" Masoud asked.

"What?"

"The Basij had confiscated the playground too. They used it to store blankets and stuff. Someone drops a lamp one day and the whole thing burns down. One guy died. Burned to death."

"Wow!"

The schoolyard used to look like a huge hangar with no walls. When the war started, we were afraid to play there. They said Saddam might think it was a factory and bomb it.

"Amir Attari kicked my soccer ball and it got stuck in the railing under the roof. It must have burned too."

***

I was twelve, we were in the schoolyard playing volleyball. I was on the left but I was not getting that many passes to strike. It was better than standing in the back though. Dad and a few other professors were going on the roof of the high school. I was not sure what they were up to. Dr. Kaveh was joking. They had a pail of muddy water with them. I asked Amir. He said they wanted to cover the water storage tank with mud so the Iraqis couldn't see it. They kept laughing. It was stupid.

Monsieur was here. The girls went up to him. I didn't know what he'd say to them. He was a revolutionary guard, a friend of the kids. I'd not seen him in the past few days since the fighter planes started coming. He was my friend too. Seyyed-something-Mousavi. We called him Monsieur. Many of the parents didn't like him. They said he was *hezbollahi*. But he was a great kid. During the student protests he'd give us rides on his motorbike and showed us what was happening. What terrible bloodshed. I fell off his bike once. It was a green Suzuki-80.

Too many of the kids surrounded Monsieur and the volleyball game was over.

The girls were squeaking with joy and excitement.

"Is this a Colt?" It was Yasmin Narimani, the Kooy's pretty girl. We had many pretty girls, but she was something else.

"It's an Airlight," Monsieur said, showing both sides of the gun.

"Shoot it!" someone said.

"I can't. I'm responsible."

We insisted. It seemed like Monsieur was in a hurry. He was saying goodbye to the kids. He said he needed to go to the front. It was sad. He was a good kid. Couldn't be more than sixteen.

The professors left. They had muddied themselves from head to toe. The water storage tank hadn't changed much.

"Goodbye, kids. This place was really cool," Monsieur was saying. "I've learned a lot from you guys. Keep the association going."

He'd started an Islamic association for the Kooy's kids. It was only Islamic by name. We'd skip classes to sit around and chat.

I was deep in thought and didn't notice what was going on. I suddenly realized everyone moving away. We covered our ears. Monsieur pointed the weapon up but hesitated a minute or two. It felt like an eternity.

He finally pulled the trigger.

***

At first, the noise used to bother me. Later, when they paved the main street, their flat, stretched, squashed bodies looked pretty bad. But we grew used to it. Once our science teacher said, "Bring some tadpoles so I can teach you about metamorphosis."

They looked just like fish at first. Fish with huge eyes. Like sperms. Then they grew a couple of hind legs. They then grew little bumps out of their sides that turned into hands and their tail started shrinking, but they still looked like fish. One day, you came up to the big plastic pan in the classroom and there were little frogs jumping around and no trace of the fish.

***

We spotted a few rowboats behind the high school.

"What are those?"

"This is the nautical department now."

We left the school area. I would have loved to go inside the elementary school. It was closed. There was a play-set with swings and a slide in front of the main entrance. It had been on one of these seesaws when I had first glanced under the skirt of one of the girls. It was very strange. Dirty.

"Let's go see our houses."

All the Moord shrubs had been destroyed. And you couldn't hear the frogs anymore. I had not seen any frog carcasses on the main street either. They must have gone extinct.

"What happened to the Moord?"

"They say the sewage flooded again and all the Moord dried out."

"The other trees are still standing though?"

"How should I know?"

"Maybe the gardeners are neglecting them."

I remembered the flood. The main street had been submerged. Katy had been standing on the other side. She was a year older than me but large for her age, with long, bushy hair. She played the piano and our parents were good friends.

"Babak, is the school open?" she called out.

"No. They shut it down because of the flood."

"I couldn't have made it anyway," she said, nodding at the river of water flowing between us.

"Yeah."

This was where the Shah had stood to talk to some of the families. They had cleaned up the Kooy really well. Changed all the blown lamps. They used to do these sorts of things back then. They had placed a post box. A few days later, Naazila Nayebi had put a letter into it. After the revolution we broke it open and the only thing we found inside was Naazila's letter.

We were behind our house. The palm tree was now taller than the second floor. We'd brought it from Tehran. We'd had it for a few years and it had not grown one bit. In Ahwaz it grew a couple of meters in one year. It was now the tallest amongst all the other trees. The eucalyptus was also quite stout now. The front yard was overridden by grass. A few of the porch glasses were broken. Clearly the new tenants weren't using the porch. One year, before the war, we had brought in someone to wall out the porch so we had an extra room. A light was on inside.

"An Indian family lives here," Kaivan said.

"They must be sorcerers," Siamak said.

I was dizzy. Our house was so small. Really small. I kept saying it and Masoud made fun of me. But I couldn't help it. It had shrunk.

"There's so much cobweb. Maybe they use it in their magic potion. 'Spider's legs, ant's tail, seal's moustache,'..."

We laughed. "Let's go to the front door."

We'd checked out Masoud's place already. I would have loved to get inside our homes. They were still our homes. The other guys didn't want to do it. I peeked over the bush. This was my parents' room. Our room was now obscured by curtains. Maybe it was their bedroom. My parents' room was still the same blue color it had been. We used to paint it once a year. I felt a certain anger towards the new tenants, but it was totally illegitimate.

We entered the front doorway.

"This is where I got the scar on my chin, you know," I said.

"It happened here?"

"Yeah. I fell off my bike and the handle tore through my chin."

I'd opened the electric meter box. "The fuses haven't changed!" The guys laughed at my joke.

In front of the house was a square field where we used to play baseball and kickball. It was very small. I ran around it in a few strides.

"Remember how a home run was such a big deal here?"

The Almasis were still here. They had never turned their home in and they had returned to Ahwaz after a couple of years. I respected them for that.

A few chadori women walked by. Things had changed here. Kids were playing in a corner. Football. We used to get on our skateboards and hide behind the wall over there. The boys on bicycles would zoom around the square and we'd grab their bikes. Often times the skateboard would not make the sharp turns and we'd end up in the Moord. It was real fun!

The kids playing were all boys. The girls were in another corner playing *vassati*. They all had scarves on. The bigger ones were sitting and talking. I knew Sara.

"Sara! How are you?"

"Hey! What are you doing here?"

"We're here to see the Kooy."

She used to be a tiny kid; like a toy doll. Very tiny. Two years younger than us, so we didn't play with her. She was quite a lady now. She ran off to tell her mom.

Masoud was beginning to feel the same as I.

"Bobby, let's show them what we're made of."

"I don't feel like it."

"Kaivan, go tell them we are their forefathers."

"Girls aren't allowed to play with the boys anymore."

"Well, it's Norooz. Maybe they're more lenient."

"We should come back tomorrow and take some pictures when there's more light."

"Yeah, the nights here are usually dark," Masoud mocked.

"Really?"

Siamak and Kaivan were goofing off. Sara showed up again.

"Hey guys, come over. Your parents are at our place."

We went. There wasn't much here anymore. The 'much' was us.

***

Dad was helping the movers. It was all dirt and not much green here. Mom was excited. She didn't say much but I knew. We'd travelled a long way. One hour in the plane. A few grown-ups showed up. They all knew Dad.

Siamak's diaper needed to be changed. Dad said we were to live here from now on. When I asked him about my daycare, he said they had a daycare here too. I didn't know if we'd have to ride a car for a whole day to see Maman Bahram again or what.

They laid a big carpet in the middle of the room. An electrician was standing on a table working on wires in the kitchen wall. Siamak was toddling through the rooms, butt-naked.

There was a big brick column in the middle of the living room. Everything here was made of bricks, including the outside of the houses. It looked nice, but I wasn't sure if this was intentional or if it was because everything was incomplete and they would cover the bricks with plaster later on.

Buzz!

Siamak had found a push-button in the hallway and he kept pressing it.

Buzz!

Mom got annoyed. "Siamak, stop it! Siamak!"

Buzz!

He wasn't paying attention to Mom. He was frowning intently and pressing the button repeatedly. Finally, the electrician disconnected the buzzer by cutting a wire where he'd been working.

Everything was very large. In front of the house, there was a huge square-shaped grass field. I didn't know if I was allowed to play there or not. I'd already made a friend here. Her name was Ziba-something-Panah. I didn't like girls much but she was all right.

Dad was inside now.

"Sudi, we got everything off the truck. Did they open the water yet?"

"Yeah. He's fixing the kitchen outlet now."

"OK."

"Dad…"

"I locked up the car door. Looks like the house across has tenants now. And I think the Mohebbis are here too."

"Dad…"

"Yes, dear?"

"Dad… Is this Ahwaz?"

"Yes, dear."

How interesting!

"Is Ahwaz part of Iran?"

"Yes," Dad answered, distractedly.

"Was Tehran part of Iran too?"

"Yes, dear. Ahwaz is part of Iran. So is Andimeshk, Boroujerd, Khorramabad, …"

"How about America, where we used to live?"

"No, dear. That's a different country."

"Is that part of the world?"

"Yes. These are all different parts of the world."

This was all very interesting to me. Dad was looking at me now.

"Dad… The world is a very big place, isn't it?"

"Yes, dear. It's very big."

THE DOVE AND THE SHRINE

I had some time on my hands, the summer before starting my postgraduate degree, so I signed up for an acting class at the university. I approached the subject rather lightly and hadn't made much of an impression on the instructor. He was some big-shot TV director whom I was supposed to know, except I never watched TV. I guess, being a serious director, he didn't quite appreciate the humor I kept trying to inject into my acting. I did manage to catch the attention of a budding young film director, though. He had a script and was using the class as a recruiting ground for actors.

"What's it about?" I asked, but he didn't want to tell me. It was his style: None of his actors should know what the movie was about until they saw the final cut.

He had a serious face, bushy eyebrows, full black beard, deep brown eyes. You could tell from his face that he was a determined man. Always serious, and intent.

"Don't shave," he said.

"OK."

"And don't cut your hair."

"When are we filming?"

"In a couple of months."

"My hair grows fast."

"Good."

"How long?" I insisted. I'd been in trouble with the revolutionary guard for wearing long hair before. It was not tolerated by the Islamic regime in those days.

"Just don't cut it. The longer the better," the director replied.

"OK." I gave up, thinking things weren't as bad anymore anyway, and plus I could always say I was in a movie and had to wear my hair long. I figured growing the beard would help too.

"I'll call to get you the pigeon," he said, as he walked quickly away.

"Pigeon?"

But he was gone.

***

The following week, one of the producers of the movie came to my door and handed me a white pigeon.

"We've clipped the wings so it can't fly off," he said, as he taught me how to hold it with one hand. "It can jump though," he continued, just in time for the bird to jump when my grip loosened. I hadn't expected the claws to tickle my palm like that. We were standing at my door, next to the busy alleyway, and I was cognizant of passersby and neighbors.

"You should spend time with it. Just hold it and stroke it gently." He showed me how. His freckled, round face looked relaxed but he was panting a bit and perspiring. It was hot, and he was on the chubby side. "It may take a little while but it's important that it gets used to you."

It was much softer than I expected. And very white. The eyes looked pinkish. I felt like I was holding something delicate and precious, and I didn't want to harm it.

"We're not going to harm it, are we?" I asked.

"Of course not," he said. Then he smiled mischievously. "We need it to survive the movie so we can kabob it for the after-party."

I didn't pretend to like the joke. The bird was too pretty and the joke too savage for my taste, so I changed the subject. "What's the movie about anyway?"

"You don't know?" he asked.

"No."

"It's a protest movie. I don't know the storyline either." He helped put the pigeon back in the cage. "It's supposed to be highly symbolic. Have you seen his other work?"

"No."

He looked me sternly in the eye and said, "He's good."

***

Two months later, in the hellish heat of a summer day in Tehran, we started shooting.

By then, I had managed to bond with the pigeon, which I had called Dr. Nejadi. I wasn't quite sure of the gender, but I'd given him a full name anyway: Dr. Mohamad Ghaasem Nejadi. Dr. Nejadi was not needed for the scenes we were to shoot that day, so he was staying home, in the comfort of my room's A/C.

I'd been told not to take a shower for a few days, and not to comb my hair. Needless to say, by the time I got to the location I was sweaty and sticky and itchy and stinky, and thoroughly hated my physical self. We were next to a busy and noisy freeway and they were setting the camera up near a narrow tunnel that ran below it. I'm not quite sure what the tunnel was for, but it didn't look like people were using it much. I joked that even homeless folks avoided this place, which the director took as a compliment on his location scouting.

"Isn't this backdrop amazing?" he exclaimed, handing me a long, thick, black winter coat and an ugly, green woolly cap.

"Are you kidding me?"

"Turn the collars up," he instructed me impatiently, and went to check on the camera.

Once I had everything on, the assistant producer put some dirt on my clothes, face, and hair, and had me kick at the ground a bit to get some on my boots.

"Where's the water?" I asked.

He pointed at a flask but said, "You're not supposed to drink."

"Why the heck not?"

"You're supposed to be thirsty."

"Am I supposed to be dead too?"

The director called me over.

"I want you to run through the tunnel at your fastest pace," he said. "You're running away. That's going to be our first sequence. We'll take a shot of you going in, and another of you running out the other side. We're trying to get the angle right." He pulled me to a specific starting point and said, "Here's where you start."

"It's hot," I complained.

"Go!"

And I ran, as fast as I could. Once I was on the other side, he waved me back.

"That was good," he said, as I wiped the sweat off my forehead. "This time, once you get to the other side, show some indecision. Lean to one side and then change directions and run the other way."

"Can I get some wa——"

"Go!"

I'm not quite sure why I ran so immediately at his order. It's not as if they were even filming. I wanted to be really professional, I guess.

As I made my way back, lingering in the shade of the tunnel just a little to get a respite from the scorching sun, he started giving me acting tips for a third run. That's when I lost it.

"What the heck? I'm dying here! Can't you get your fucking camera to work and shoot the damn thing? At least get me some water!"

He stared at me for a few seconds in what seemed to be a look of admiration.

"What?" I asked, annoyed.

"I think you're getting ready," he said, with a half-smile.

Was this all a setup just to get me in the proper mood for the movie? The thought was offensive to me. Did he think I was not a good actor?

"Umm... no," came a voice from behind the camera. "There's something wrong with the battery. We're not ready yet."

"What?"

"Just give me a few more minutes."

"SHIT!" I threw my cap down. "I'm baking!" I took the coat off, slapped it down, and sat on the ground in the shade of the tunnel entrance. This must have concerned the director. He probably didn't want me to cool off. He walked up to me, squatted next to me, and started whispering in my ear.

"You know what a good actor would be able to do in this situation?"

he asked.

I just glared at him, still angry.

"A good actor," he paused, "would act out a skit in which he'd pretend it's winter, and he's caught in a blizzard, and he doesn't have enough clothes, and he's freezing."

"Go to hell."

"Just saying."

I started thinking about it. I was completely pissed with this guy, but I couldn't resist the challenge. I shut my eyes and thought about how I'd do it. It was so hot and sunny I had a hard time imagining cold. Then I thought about the similarities of freezing and burning and imagined that my current discomfort was a result of being extremely cold. In my mind, I went over every single malady and changed its association. It was like refactoring computer code. I did the same with the environmental elements. The shining sun stinging my eyes was reassigned as a blizzard, needling my face. The sunshine was the wind, carrying particles of icy snow. And the shade... the shade was an open fire someone had lit to survive this bitter cold.

So, I went to the fire, protecting my face from the blizzard, wearing my cap tight, and buttoning up my overcoat. I held my hands on the flame, wishing I could step into it and heat up my entire frozen body.

"God it's freezing," I said, with a quivering voice, rubbing my hands and stepping in place.

"All right!" called someone in admiration, as the five or six cast and crew members started clapping their hands for me, giving me a jump.

***

Qom is two hundred kilometers south of Tehran, on the edge of the desert. It is a highly religious town built around the shrine of one of the Shiite saints' female relatives. The religious school adjacent to the shrine is probably the largest of its kind. It is the religious capital of Iran, which in Islamic Iran means that it is also a center of power.

I don't like Qom. It is dirty; the water is salty and undrinkable; there are no rivers or hills; the weather is dry and hot; and the people seem deceptive and sleazy. The town should really not exist, but for the thousands of needy and sick who come to pray and pay their dues to the saint; or to bury their dead; or for the others, who go to the school there to learn the art of religious deception, these days mostly in a quest for power.

The entire cast and crew took the bus to Qom one evening, a few weeks after shooting the tunnel scene. The producer had a relative who was some kind of an authority at the religious school. He had gotten us a permit to film in the main mosque area. We stayed the night at their place. No one was there and they had given us a key to get in, with instructions to sleep on the roof and not touch the furniture.

Sleeping on the roof was fun. It seemed uncomfortable at first. You had to go all the way downstairs to pee and I had to step over people, and I hated the toilet, with its threat of cockroaches looming in every shaded corner.

I didn't like the fart fest either. That started as soon as we were all snuggled under the blankets. But the weather was cool, the desert sky was full of bright stars, and we enjoyed talking long into the night about the many ways we all hated Qom.

The next day, we handed our filming permit to some authority, and he let us set up our equipment in a big yard enclosed by the shrine and the religious school. We took a few shots of the background, and the director then turned to me to give me my instructions.

The first scene we shot was of me, standing in one of the smaller entrances to the yard, smoking a cigarette. I didn't like smoking, but that day, I must have gone through half a pack. The problem was the director wanted it to be almost at the filter before I tossed the butt, and the smoke had to come out of my mouth in just the right shape of plume.

***

The last time I had smoked a cigarette was when I was in middle school. My grandma had picked up smoking when she found out two of her sons were imprisoned, and I wanted to try it too.

I had remembered the day my youngest uncle started smoking, a few months before he was apprehended and imprisoned based on false accusations. He'd come home one day with a pack, declaring, "I'm going to start smoking today."

"Bahram!" my mom had exclaimed.

"I will smoke one cigarette, on the balcony, at five p.m., every day," he had said.

He had a style of smoking that was relaxing even to watch. Contemplative.

Intentional. Deliberate. Focused. It was about enjoying the smoke.

So, I stole one of my uncle's cigarettes and lit it in his bedroom while he was away one day.

I heard one of our smoking relatives respond to my mother's concern once, saying he was fine, because he never let the smoke in, and so I figured that was how I would start.

I kept blowing into the thing and wondering what the big deal was. It wasn't bothering me the least bit. Maybe it was the 'playing with fire' thing that got people all anxious.

That's when I decided to let some of the smoke in, and I inhaled, more than I should have, falling into a wild fit of coughing that just wouldn't stop.

Disgusted, I got rid of the cigarette and ran to the kitchen for some water. A few minutes later, Grandma came downstairs looking for me.

"Babak!"

"Yes?" I tried hard to sound innocent.

"Were you smoking?"

"What?"

"You were smoking, weren't you?"

"No! Smoking what?"

"Are you sure?"

"Yes! I've been here reading my book all afternoon. I don't smoke, it's bad for you. Maybe it was Uncle Bahram."

"OK," she said. "If you see your uncle, please tell him not to toss a lit cigarette into a plastic wastebasket. It makes an awful mess."

After a few more careful sessions of smoking, I started worrying that it was becoming a habit.

I've always worried about addiction, probably not for the same reasons most people warn you against it: I've always felt that being predictable is dangerous.

I decided to shake the habit and stole five of my grandma's cigarettes and chain-smoked them in the bathroom, disposing of the butts in the drain. I then threw up in the toilet, flushed, and never smoked again.

Ten years later, after my uncle was released from prison, where he had turned into a chain-smoker himself, he marched down the stairs with a box full of cigarette packs, ashtrays, and lighters.

He set the box down and declared, "I will never smoke again." And went back upstairs to his room.

He has not lit a cigarette since.

***

After a couple of hours and multiple cigarettes, standing at one of the entrances to the holy shrine's open courtyard, we finally got the smoking scene right and went on to film me, stealing a pigeon from the shrine's courtyard.

The courtyard was a large, plant-less, paved expanse, the size of several football fields, with the beautiful golden-domed shrine standing diagonally across from where we were, bracketed by its tall, proud sky-blue minarets. It was busy with some people washing at a fountain next to the shrine before entering to pray. Every once in a while, a funeral procession would circle the area with men carrying the coffin and chanting "La-elaaha-ela-lah"—there is no god but Allah—and a group of black-veiled wailing women following them around.

We stood there, taking it all in for a few minutes, and then got busy with the film. We were behind schedule and there was no time to waste.

The plan was to get close to a flock of pigeons, grab one, and run. The pigeon I was to grab was the white dove I had been living with for the past few months: Dr. Nejadi. By now, we had bonded to the point where it was no longer pooping in my hand when I grabbed it.

There was a huge flock of dark-grey pigeons in the courtyard when we got there, and our white dove would clearly stand out in their midst. The producer had a bag of pigeon feed, and he spread a fistful around the area where we planned to film the kidnapping. Within minutes, the entire flock of several hundred birds were merrily pecking away.

As soon as we let our white pigeon loose into the flock, however, every other bird flew away.

"What the heck?"

"They don't like him?"

"Maybe he's a different species."

"He's a different color, that's for sure."

"Racists!"

I fetched our pigeon and scolded him. "Don't scare them, Dr. Nejadi!"

"Look!" called the assistant producer. The flock was back again, pecking at the seeds.

I let the pigeon go again, but as soon as it hit the ground, the flock flew away.

"How come they're not afraid of us, then?"

I pretended to sniff my pigeon's butt, as if it was stinky, and got a few laughs.

The flock was back in the courtyard now, and the assistant producer was starting to run out of pigeon feed.

"Put Dr. Nejadi down somewhere at a distance and let him move towards the flock at his own pace," the director instructed me.

Dr. Nejadi started pecking his way towards the flock, but like a growing oil slick, the other pigeons parted around him, staying at a safe distance.

"Would this work?" I asked, pointing at the dove.

The director shook his head. "They've got to be packed in together."

I was about to accuse him of being a perfectionist, when, with the white dove presumably too close for comfort, the flock suddenly took flight again, leaving Dr. Nejadi to feast on all the bird feed he wished for.

"Shit!" I said.

"Let's be patient. Just give it some time," said the director.

So, we found shade and sat around, chatting and hiding our desperation, pretending not to be glancing at the pigeon flock every few seconds.

Time passed, slower than usual, with the crowds coming and going, and the occasional wailing and cries of "La elaha ellalaah" from mourners following a coffin.

"That must be the fourth procession since we got here," I remarked.

"Dude, this is a slow day."

"Slow day for business," said someone, smirking.

"Best business in the world!" said the director. "It's steadier than selling life insurance. Zero risk."

"Death insurance," I added, after a pause.

***

An hour or so later (or at least, it felt that long), after counting five more funeral processions going through their ceremonial circling of the courtyard, the flock was still perched safely away from Dr. Nejadi, on a high ledge at the far side from where we were.

"I got the permission!" called the producer, walking toward us from one of the buildings.

The permit we had was only good for the courtyard, but the producer's relative was pretty high up the mullah rankings, and the director had sent him to see if the city would let us go up one of the minarets.

"Cool!" we said, almost in unison.

"Can we take our filming gear there too?" asked the ever-demanding director.

"We can try." The producer smiled.

So, we did, and they let us in the shrine.

"I hate this barefoot business," said the director, as we all took our shoes off. I turned to look at him, and I noticed that he was visibly nervous and a bit angry. That surprised me. I'd always thought of him as a religious guy.

"Leeches," I heard him say under his breath, looking at a cleric.

As we walked, he inadvertently kicked some guy's prayer stone clear across the huge hall, and of course, the man didn't even flinch, demonstrating how devoutly he was concentrating on his prayers.

"Do you believe in this crap?" he asked me in a whisper.

I wasn't sure what to say, and I wasn't sure how inadvertent his kick was, so I just smiled awkwardly. I didn't think he was waiting for an answer anyway.

"Leeches," he muttered again with disgust.

We went up the stairs to the roof, and around to the foot of one of the minarets. The iron door was narrow and low, and we had to go in one at a time. I stopped to read the signpost as the other three ducked in.

Minaret Info, it read, along with some identification number. After a few lines of information-less introduction, there was a table, each row giving a short description of an event along with its date. The whole thing wasn't that old, built around two hundred years ago. Since construction, it had been repaired a dozen times and had even been completely ruined and rebuilt a few times.

The last printed row had a self-congratulatory note on how the Islamic Republic had done a scientific review of the minaret and reinforced the structure. They even displayed the budget for the project. The date was from last year. Below that, was a handwritten sticker adding a new row to the table, dated only two months ago:

Measurements show a 12-degree deviation due to recent seismic activity.

"Um, guys, are you sure about this?" I called after them. But it was too late.

"Come on up," came an echoing voice. "This is awesome!"

I climbed, on all fours, up the steepest, twistiest, dirtiest stairway I'd ever seen. It was pitch dark and full of cobwebs, and I even stepped on some animal bones on the way up. The minaret narrowed, the higher I climbed, and even though at least one of the guys ahead of me was bigger than me, I started to worry about getting stuck.

At the top, there was another iron door, through which the sudden sunlight stung my eyes. I walked out onto the round porch as my vision adjusted, taking in a gorgeous view that seemed to go on and on forever. Qom was a pretty flat town, and the minarets were intentionally the highest structures around. The cameraman was setting up his equipment and the director was holding his hands out, forming a square by inverting his thumb and pointing finger of one hand over the other, looking through it with one eye. Then suddenly, the assistant producer pointed down at the courtyard and shouted, "Look!"

We couldn't believe our eyes. There it was: the entire flock of grey pigeons, with Dr. Mohamad Ghaasemeh Nejadi in their midst, in total racial harmony.

I looked at the director.

"Go!" he cried, and I shot down the scary stairwell, dashed across the roof of the shrine, and then walked, as quickly as I could, through the shrine's main hall—careful not to soccer kick any of the prayer stones—and out the shrine doors onto the courtyard.

I looked up, barely seeing the figures of the director and the others atop the minaret. There was no way for me to see them signaling the take, so I just waved at them and got to work, walking slowly through the flock, up to Dr. Nejadi, hesitating and looking around, then leaping in exaggeration, almost over him, to snatch him and run out.

Except, Dr. Nejadi didn't want to be snatched.

The damned bird jumped away from me and I missed, slipping on fresh bird dung and landing on my butt. Ow!

I looked up with a grin and waved at the minaret again. I slowly walked to my starting position to repeat the process, but once again, the bird jumped away, and I missed him. On the third go, I was determined to stay in character and get the bird, whatever it took, and ended up zigzagging through the flock, cursing loudly, and grabbing for Dr. Nejadi repeatedly.

"Wait! You blasted bird! Get back here, goddamn it!"

I lunged for it again and slipped again.

"SHIT!" I cried in rage, pumping my fist at it.

Suddenly, an enormous roar of laughter woke me up to the reality outside the flock: there was a large and gathering crowd of onlookers, pointing at me, thoroughly entertained. All the failed attempts at catching the dove, while wearing winter clothes and occasionally waving and grinning at the minaret, must have made for a strange scene.

I got up, all embarrassed and blushing, and started patting the dust off my winter coat, when someone grabbed me by the arm in a fierce grip.

"What do you think you are doing?"

It was an officer, perhaps responsible for the shrine's security. "You are disrupting the order! Can't you see people are here to mourn their dead and pray?"

"I... but—"

"Shut up!" This guy was really angry. "You are under arrest, you little bastard. One night in prison will teach you to respect the holy saints."

"Wait—"

"Shut up!" he cried, slamming me in the head with the palm of his hand.

Uh-oh! I thought. *I'm in real trouble.* I imagined a dark, deep dungeon in some secret corner of the building where I was to be thrown and maybe forgotten forever. I am not kidding. I really had that thought, and it wasn't funny.

I was on the verge of tears as we headed into a side building, when our producer came panting after the officer.

"Excuse me, brother!" he was calling. "Brother! Allow me to explain the situation."

He showed him the permit, pointing at the rest of the crew, who were walking toward us, with the camera and tripod over the cameraman's shoulder.

"Movie, eh?" the officer asked, flipping the permit in his hand, looking at both sides. "What kind of movie is this?"

"It's a religious movie," the producer said.

"About what?" The officer looked at him suspiciously. "Is this serious or are you guys a bunch of clowns making a lighthearted comedy?"

In Iran, especially between religious people, being lighthearted was usually equated with being disrespectful or thoughtless.

"No," the producer said with a suddenly concerned voice. "This is a serious movie. It's about a poor guy who comes to a shrine to pray, and his prayers are answered."

The officer looked at the permit again. He pointed at the name on the paper and asked, "Do you know the Ayatollah?"

"He's my grandfather's nephew," the producer said, with a smile.

"Is he now?" The officer's demeanor changed noticeably. "You should have told me earlier."

He looked at me again, then turned and pointed at the producer. "Can I have a private word with you?" he asked, and took him aside.

***

We finished filming that day by taking shots of me from the waist up, with the producer lying on the ground, hidden from the camera, holding Dr. Nejadi. I would walk through the flock and grab the dove out of his hands.

"We'll edit the thing together," the director said reassuringly. "It'll look good. You'll see."

A few days later, my scenes for the movie were done. I didn't hear from the team for the rest of the summer and, with school starting again, I was too busy to follow up. It was a new chapter in my life. I was a master's student now, and somehow everything that went on that summer, including the acting, the movie, and the trip to Qom, seemed to be from another place, a different time.

I never saw the movie. I don't even know if it was ever completed. In fact, I still don't know what the movie was about, or its name. I'm embarrassed to say that, in spite of spending all that time with them, I don't remember the names of any of the crew members either. Not even the director's. Actually, come to think of it, in the excitement of making an actual movie, I probably forgot his name immediately after he was introduced to me, on that very first day, and was too embarrassed to ask later.

I do remember the name of the doctor though, Dr. Mohamad Ghaasem Nejadi.

SEIDOON

What am I doing here anyway? I thought, gazing out the window of the minibus as it sped through the motorway between *Izeh* and *Ramhormoz*, towards *Baghmalek*. These were remote towns in Khuzestan I would never have visited, if not for my buddy Masoud, whom I had not seen for months.

It was the early nineties; I had graduated and was awaiting my second draft, so I had some time on my hands.

Back then, if you were graduating from med school, you had a choice of spending five years somewhere in Iran, working for the health ministry instead of your two-year obligatory military service. The duration could be shortened depending on your assignment. In a big city or in Tehran, you had to do all five years. In more remote towns, it would be four years, or what they called a four-fifth. Masoud had picked a village northeast of Khuzestan province. His service was a three-fifth.

I had flown into Ahwaz, the capital of Khuzestan, a few days before, accompanying my dad on one of his monthly trips. In those years, Dad was what was commonly known in Iran as a "Flying Professor." He would fly down to Ahwaz once a month and teach his students for ten days or so before flying back home to Tehran.

Every month, one or two days prior to his departure date, my parents would get into a bit of a quarrel. It had turned into a familiar ritual, but

191

they did it anyway, even while acknowledging it at the same time.

"Amir, why are you not packing your warm clothes?" Mom would ask. "Do I have to go through your bag again?"

"Just let me be, Sudy," Dad would reply, annoyed. "I already have warm clothes in Ahwaz."

"No, you don't. You brought them back last year. Are we starting our monthly quarrel here?"

"Of course we are. You treat me like a child, that's why." Dad would raise his voice. "Just, let me deal with the packing, will you?"

And it would heat up from there and hit a climax the night before, and end in a declaration from Dad that he is happy he is getting away from Mom, or a declaration from Mom that she would savor some sanity while Dad was away. Everything would be back to normal, as if nothing had happened, the moment Dad called from Ahwaz letting us know that his trip had been smooth and that he'd made it to his suite at the university campus. Sometimes I think maybe this mode of living strengthened their bond, giving them space to appreciate each other more.

I was thinking about this, and about my dad, on that minibus ride. About how I had not expected to find Dad's place so tidy, with rules like where the shoes should go, or his system for washing the dishes or how the toiletries were arranged by the bathroom sink. I had not expected it. These were all Mom's responsibilities back home, and Dad was one of us: a law-abiding resident.

I wondered, maybe the system back home was initially designed and operated by them both, but, over time, had the day-to-day operations been assumed by Mom?

I looked at my watch, calculating that we'd be arriving at *Baghmalek* in twenty minutes. Masoud would be waiting to pick me up at the station. He had not said how we'd get to *Seidoon* from there. I knew he didn't have a car, so maybe we'd be taking another minibus. Was that how he got around? Must have been tough for him after practically owning his dad's car for all these years.

Masoud and I wrote letters to each other while he was away, but he also called occasionally, and we had planned my visit over one of those calls.

"This area is unlike most of Khuzestan, Babak, it's mountainous, and the people are mostly of Lor ethnicity," he had said on the grainy call.

"It's interesting. You'll see."

All I could see out the bus window was barren flatland stretching out to the horizon. *Different geography, different people,* I thought, *must be interesting.*

***

"How was Ahwaz?" Masoud asked, after we boarded the minibus to *Seidoon.* He had met me at the stop in *Baghmalek* and we'd had to run to make the connection.

"Good!" I said. "Your dad showed me the beehives again." I smiled.

Masoud's dad was an entomologist, but unlike mine who specialized in tiny, boring aphids, Dr. Kaameli was a bee expert. His explanations of the lives of honeybees were fascinating: how they are so much more social than most other animals, to the point where a hive of bees acts as a coherent single unit. "The notion of an 'individual' honeybee really doesn't make much sense by human standards," Dr. Kaameli had said once. The best story I could get from my dad on aphids was that ants enslave them, feed them, then tickle them until they throw up and store their vomit for food. Gross. "They are basically the equivalent of domesticated cows in the insect world!" Dad would say, excitedly. Why would you want to study such dumb creatures? I'd wonder.

"Cool! You saw my dad?" Masoud asked.

"I did," I replied. "I had time to kill this morning, so I went to the agriculture department with Dad and ran into Dr. Kaameli."

"Did you visit the Kooy too?"

"Nah, nothing interesting there." I looked out the window. "How far is *Seidoon?*"

"About thirty-five kilometers," Masoud said. "We'll be there in forty-five minutes or so."

"Is the road that bad?" I asked.

"At least it's paved." He grinned.

The last passenger boarded. The driver, a mustached middle-aged man with narrow eyes and a major case of crow's feet extending his long grey eyelashes, took the last puff on his cigarette and jumped into the driver's seat, calling out "*Seidoon!*" Then he started the diesel engine and put it into gear.

The minibus wasn't crowded. I noticed most men wore thick

mustaches and a few had head wraps, but they didn't look like what the Arabs back in Ahwaz wore. There were only two or three women on board, all wearing black chadors. All carrying babies and traveling with their men.

"What does *Seidoon* mean?" I wondered half to myself.

"The word comes from *Seid*: to hunt," Masoud said, always knowing these sorts of things. "These people were hunters and nomads. Very tribal. Moving around all the time and getting into fights with other tribes."

I looked at one of the passengers who looked quite innocent. Just a tired man, looking older than his age, with deep lines in his face and calloused hands.

"This area was settled recently, mostly after the revolution," Masoud continued.

"What do they do now?" I asked.

"They mourn, mostly," Masoud said, matter-of-factly.

I laughed, but Masoud didn't.

"I'm serious," he said, laughing a bit himself now. "They don't have much to do, most of them. They just live off government handouts and one-up each other in mourning for their dead."

"How sad," I said. "Maybe they're subconsciously mourning their lost way of living?"

"Maybe." Masoud replied. "They mourn seven straight days after a death, then the whole week leading up to the fortieth day. Then the week of the first-year anniversary, and each time like the person died just now."

We hit a rather large bump and a baby I had not even noticed on board started crying in her mother's arms under her black chador.

"It gets pretty bizarre sometimes actually," he continued. "One time, I heard the mourning chant go: What a young man has died, his motorbike was a Honda."

"Really?" I laughed.

Masoud nodded. "I'm not joking! Mourning is a competitive sport out here."

***

Sure enough, when we got to *Seidoon*, the minibus stopped next to a large *hosseinieh*, or Shiite gathering hall, with its loudspeakers blaring out mourning chants.

The living quarters adjacent to the *Seidoon* clinic did not have a lot of furniture. Masoud and the other doctor stationed there, Javad, were the only occupants. The first thing I noticed was a clunky, noisy old fridge, which shook violently every once in a while.

"Needs to be exorcised," Masoud said.

"We think it has something to do with the milk we forgot to throw out," Javad added.

There was no TV in the living room. Just an old carpet, some pillows, and an old Backgammon set in the corner.

Masoud showed me the bathroom. It was a traditional hole-in-the-ground toilet, with a shower next to it.

"When you're taking a shower, make sure you hold on to the soap or you're gonna have to fish it out of there." Masoud pointed into the toilet hole.

"Gross!" I grimaced.

"And this iron bar will come in handy from time to time." Masoud pointed at a bar leaning against the bathroom wall. It had a bend three quarters of the way on its length. Masoud mimed using it to unclog the toilet.

"OK, boss," Javad said, after showing me his room with the folded mattress I was to sleep on at night. "I'm gonna head out."

"What kind of a boss is Masoud?" I asked.

"Oh, he's strict!" Javad laughed.

Masoud? A strict boss? I couldn't quite see it.

"Thanks so much for letting me take your room while you're away," I said.

"Don't mention it, buddy."

Once he left, Masoud got some *Taftoon* flatbread and Feta cheese from the scary fridge, we set the tablecloth on the carpet in the tiny living room, and we had dinner. I couldn't help but notice how he brought the cucumbers to his nose one by one to decide if they were still good to eat.

"So how do you get around here?" I asked. "The Donkey Express?"

"You'll see," Masoud said, mysteriously. "We're going to go check on a few villages tomorrow."

"You're responsible for other villages too?"

Masoud nodded. "*Seidoon* is central to a group of ten or so villages in this area. As the head of the clinic, I'm responsible for all of them and have to pay each one a visit at least once a month."

"Cool. How many are we visiting tomorrow?" I asked, munching on the flatbread cheese roll.

"Three or four."

***

That night, as we played Backgammon over who should wash the dishes, I had a few stories from my six-month mandatory student service for Masoud, and he had a few stories of his past year in *Seidoon*.

"They're still at it!" I pointed in the direction of the mourning chants from the *hosseinieh* loudspeaker.

"I told you, it's a constant. You'd better get used to it."

I rolled my eyes.

"The roads here can get pretty twisty," Masoud said. "One time, we had a patient in the ambulance who kept asking for a *Peelow-si*."

"A what?"

"A *Peelow-si*." Masoud smiled. "You don't know what that is?"

I shook my head

"Well, neither did we, until the guy threw up all over the ambulance," Masoud said, throwing the dice.

"I don't get it." I replied, feeling a bit stupid.

"He was asking for a plastic bag!" Masoud burst into laughter. "You know, *Peelow-si*, Plastic."

I laughed at the way he pronounced it. "You need a translator here. How can you diagnose your patients' diseases if you can't understand what they're saying?"

"Oh, most of the time the problem isn't understanding what they're saying," Masoud said. "Often what they say just doesn't make sense."

"Like how?" I asked.

"Well, they would walk into the clinic and I'd ask them what's wrong, and they'd point at their knee and say, 'It's my knee, doc.' I'd check their knee and find nothing wrong with it. After a whole bunch of back and forth, I'd find out they have a backache!"

"What?"

"I'm serious!" Masoud laughed. "I ask them why they pointed at their knees, and they'd say: 'I broke my knee as a kid, and now, every once in a while, a wind blows through my body, starting at my knee, and hits my back, and I get a backache.'"

I laughed again. Masoud had really gotten the local accent down.

"Want some grapes?" Masoud asked.

"Sure." I looked at the backgammon board and the sorry state I was in, and added, "Don't need a new dish for them, just hand them too me." And we both laughed out loud. It was good to be back together after so many months.

I don't remember all the stories he told me that night. Something about visiting a remote village by helicopter after a flood. A story about how some women here were named *dokhtar-bas* which means 'enough girls,' because the parents wanted a boy; a story about how some people kept asking for shots for their prescriptions because they didn't like taking drugs on a schedule.

"Does it confuse them?" I asked.

"Most of them are illiterate and can't read the instructions," Masoud said.

"Your turn."

And Masoud threw the dice.

***

The next morning, Masoud unlocked the mysterious door in the living room to reveal the clinic.

"The door is my secret getaway," he said, as we stepped into the doctor's office, complete with a poster of the human body, a plastic skeleton on a hanger, an examination bed with a stool next to it, an old desk, and a worn-out seat. Masoud locked the door behind him.

"Why aren't you working today?" I asked.

"The clinic is only open on Mondays, Wednesdays, Fridays." Masoud lead the way through the waiting area, where they had twenty or so old folding school chairs in two rows. "This little place," he said, waving his arm, "serves *Seidoon* and all its ten satellite villages." He looked at me. "More than fifteen thousand people.

"Looks dirty. But smells clean," I said.

"It's not dirty. Just poor."

He unlocked the front door, revealing the clinic's light-yellow ambulance. "Our transportation!" he announced.

"Cool!"

"Wait here, I'll call the driver." Masoud walked away quickly down the alleyway.

"You have a driver?" But he was gone.

I turned to the clinic, thinking about Masoud and how his job was to care for people in need. How satisfying it must be, doing something you knew helped people directly and immediately. I wrote code. Who knew if the code would ever help anyone? I was in the service of this ambiguous concept called "progress." He was in the unambiguous service of people.

I noticed a little garden at the entrance to the clinic, with a few roses that seemed to have recently been planted, with sticks next to them, holding them up. *Masoud made this garden*, I thought. It looked like something he would do.

***

With Masoud and me sitting in the front next to the driver, Hassan, we travelled the twisty mountain road in the clunky old ambulance. Hassan was in his early thirties, but he looked older. He had bad teeth, grey thinning hair, a large mustache under a big nose, and a funny, wide smile. He was literate, having finished fifth grade.

Hassan was respectful and deferential towards Masoud, which was weird for me to see. I bet Masoud felt awkward about it too. With me being there, his work and personal lives were mixing up a bit. All the same, the two seemed to have a warm and friendly relationship, and they laughed together as they reminisced about funny things that had happened to them on their many inspection trips.

He was not that good a driver, though. I bet he thought he was, because he drove very fast and made sharp turns on the challenging, mountainous road. But, as my dad always said, "A good driver is a driver whose passengers don't notice their driving."

"What are you up to in Tehran these days?" Masoud asked me as we both stared ahead at the road, willing intently for the car to remain on it.

"I'm working for Neda, a startup that's operating Iran's first BBS." I spoke loudly so he could hear me. "That's like a community of computer users connected remotely."

"Oh, like with that device you told me about... what was it called again?"

"Yeah, a dial-up modem," I said. "People dial out our phone center using their modems and get connected to each other through our service. It's pretty cool. You can send electronic letters to each other—that's called e-mail—then we have communities where you can message folks on a common topic of interest. We're even connected to the Internet—that's like a BBS for the world."

"Wow! Fascinating." He thought about it for a moment. "Are the authorities OK with that?"

"They don't know much about it. Only a limited number of people have access. The bandwidth is really limited. Plus," I added, "Neda has friends in high places. The mayor is on our board."

"That helps," he said.

"He's commissioned us to build a municipal database on our BBS that people can access from kiosks around Tehran," I said.

"That guy is ambitious," Masoud said, referring to the mayor. "Sooner or later his wings are gonna get clipped."

I didn't like the pessimism. He was probably right. Still, I didn't like it.

After a bumpy twenty-minute ride, we arrived at a remote village. Our first stop.

"There's no power or running water here," Masoud said.

The houses were made of mud, it seemed, and there were no paved streets. A bunch of kids started running after the ambulance. Their clothes were dirty, but it wasn't clear to me if this was because they were poor or because it was hard to keep your clothes clean with all the dirt.

We stopped next to a small building with a sign that said: House of Healthcare.

"They're not here," Masoud said.

"Hey, kids!" Hassan called. "Go fetch the health workers, will you?"

"Yes, sir!" They ran off at top speed as if it was a race.

"They must be around," Masoud said. "Each village has a House of Healthcare." He pointed at the building. "And each House of Healthcare has two health workers. One man, one woman."

"Where do they come from?" I asked, thinking there's no way they could be from this village.

"From the village they serve, usually," Masoud said, surprising me. "They have to have a fifth-grade diploma, at least. My job is to select promising candidates and send them to a six-month training course in Ahwaz, where they learn some basics and take a licensing exam."

"What do they do?"

"They should be able to administer first aid and give people vaccine shots," Masoud replied. "But most importantly, they are health educators."

A young man and woman showed up and greeted us. The man unlocked the door and showed us in. It was a single small, white room with a window opposite the entrance, and three chairs. The walls were covered with posters. I was amazed at the fact that one of the posters was about symptoms of AIDS.

Masoud asked the health workers a few questions, mainly on a recent flu outbreak, vaccination rates, and an upcoming family planning workshop they were holding. The meeting took fifteen minutes or so.

"Were they related?" I asked Masoud, once we were back in the ambulance heading to our next stop.

"No, I don't think so."

We both had one hand on the dashboard, steadying ourselves as the driver navigated the many bumps in the dirt road.

"Is that an issue around here?"

"They're very conservative in this area," Masoud replied. "But there's also a lot of trust in medical workers."

"I wasn't expecting an AIDS information poster," I said.

"They also give away contraception." I could detect a hint of pride in his tone. "There's a big campaign to reduce the birth rate. We're not making too much headway on that, though, unfortunately."

"Yeah, I guess improved healthcare should go hand in hand with family planning," I said. "I'm just surprised how well organized and pragmatic this stuff is all the way out here. Did not expect it in the Islamic Republic."

"It's not political," Masoud said. "That's why it remains under the radar and politicians don't mess with it."

***

At the next village, I decided to sit out the inspection and stroll around a bit, taking a few photos. I wondered why the place was so deserted. *Maybe everyone's working in the fields*, I thought.

It was hot, so I fetched a fruit juice from Masoud's bag in the ambulance and walked towards the end of the main drag to check out the hills that surrounded the thirty or so houses. This was the southern edge of the Zagros Mountain range and had a unique look and feel to it. The mountains were less rocky than the Alborz, north of Tehran, and the vegetation was sparser. Unlike the lush, thick vegetation of the northern foothills of the Alborz, the forests here were sparse, with spaced out trees, old twisting oaks that bent and bowed through the years yet survived the harsh weather and still sprang new leaves every year. You could almost see the torture and perseverance of survival in their shapes, each one seeming to have a story to tell.

I hiked up the hill a bit to get to the first tree. The locals had tied pieces of different colored cloth to the branches, each probably representing a prayer. "How many did you grant, old guy?" I patted the thick, jagged trunk.

I turned to walk back but just stood there, mesmerized at the site of the vast barley field in the wind. I'd never seen anything like it. A majestic wave would start at one end of the blond sea and make its way violently to the fore, setting off many smaller waves in different directions along the way, yet merging into a single flow closer to the edge. Then, after some moments of calm sanity, it would start again. But this time, the pattern would be different. Unlike the sea, the waves were not made of a uniform substance. You could see individual straws of barley bending this way and that, and you knew that they were all firmly rooted in the land. Yet the waves kept moving through them, at once static and in flight.

No point in taking a photo, I thought, *there's no way a photo would capture this.*

As I walked back into the village, turning a corner, I ran into a young girl who froze in place as soon as she saw me. She had a colorful ethnic dress on. A bright green silk skirt and black baggy pants, a white long-sleeved satin shirt, with a dark blue sleeveless jacket worn over it, a thin, see-through veil secured on her head with a tiara, and two streams of jet-black hair framing her beautiful, round face. She had deep brown eyes, perfectly symmetrical, thin, arched, connected eyebrows, long eyelashes, red cheeks and puckered lips.

I simply could not take my eyes off her. Not knowing what to say, I gently raised my camera. "May I take a picture of you, please?" I asked.

She looked at the camera with dread, shook her head, and ran off.

"She must have been fourteen or fifteen, but looked older," I said to Masoud, after we boarded the ambulance. "Heartstoppingly beautiful, in a genuine way. The exact opposite of the girls we fantasize about."

"You should be really careful around unmarried girls here." Masoud's voice was hushed so the driver wouldn't hear him over the noise of the road. "Most murders in this area are over family pride matters."

I raised my eyebrows and let out an audible gulp. We both laughed.

***

Our last stop was a village shaped like a cake on a low hill, with a stream running through it. The sun was setting as we got there, and the colors and shades made for a beautiful view.

A group of twenty or so women, old and young, crowded around the middle part of the stream, washing dishes in the flowing water. There seemed to be a system for the dish washing, with some people responsible for soaping, some rinsing, and some drying the dishes. There was also a lot of high-pitched chatter and occasional outbursts of laughter amongst them. They all had their sleeves rolled up, were wearing scarves, and had their black chadors tied around their waists.

"We've called a special meeting with the village leaders." Masoud pointed at a house on top of the cake. "Wanna come?"

"Sure."

It was a bit of a hike up the narrow, muddy alleyways to the meeting place and it gave us quite a workout. *This is the most important building in the village,* I thought, *and the hardest to get to.*

We were greeted at the door by the village chief, who showed us in and offered us to sit next to him, on the floor, at the head of the room full of cross-legged men sitting in a circle with their backs to the walls. A dish with neatly placed rows of dates was passed around. I was hungry and picked one and stuck it in my mouth, only to realize that everyone was politely placing their dates on a plate to have with the tea that was also being passed around.

After a few minutes of exchanging greetings and a short speech by the chief, thanking us for our visit, Masoud started asking them some questions about their health needs. He wanted to get a sense of where they were in building their House of Healthcare, and why it was taking so long, and that they were one of the last villages in his jurisdiction not to have one yet. He asked about vaccination rates and was not satisfied with the vague answer and said they needed to do a better job of bookkeeping.

"We are all very busy and don't have the time, Doctor," one of the men said.

"Without the health center, you will have to do the bookkeeping," Masoud replied. "Otherwise, we can't get you the vaccines, and your children will get sick."

"It is a long road, but we will bring our sick to *Seidoon*," the chief said.

Masoud sighed. "Which one's easier, Chief, to bring your sick to *Seidoon* or to build a House of Healthcare and send us two volunteers to train so they can get your children vaccinated so they don't get sick in the first place?"

"But you don't understand," another man with a white beard said, "everyone is busy here. No one can volunteer. Even our youth are out in the fields all the time and helping."

"If you spare two of your youth for the health center, you will have ten more healthy hands to help in the fields." Masoud nodded his head to get them to agree. "Am I right?"

"We will try," said the chief. "You are right. We will try our best."

"Next time I'm out here we need the health center done," Masoud's voice was firm.

"We will try, Doctor," the white-bearded man said. "Have another tea, please."

"One more thing," Masoud added.

"Yes, Doctor."

"You need to work on the birth rate. Your village has one of the highest birth rates in all of Khuzestan."

"I don't understand." The chief turned to the man next to him with a confused look. "Do you understand what the good doctor is saying?"

"Too many children," Masoud said. "You need to reduce it."

The chief laughed nervously.

"Every family should have, at most, two children," Masoud continued.

"I wish God would grant us that," the chief said.

"Well, the good news is that God has made it possible for you to plan your family size," Masoud replied.

"It is hard," said the man next to the chief. "We keep praying for less, but God keeps adding to our children."

"How many kids do you have?" Masoud asked him.

"I have eight kids," he replied. "And seven daughters too, unfortunately."

Masoud's eyebrows popped up. "You have fifteen kids?"

"I keep praying for less," the man said again.

Masoud shook his head. "Prayer is not enough. If all you do is pray for a healthy crop, you won't get anything. You have to work at it." He turned to our ambulance driver. "Am I right, Hassan?"

"Yes, Doctor," he said helpfully.

Masoud turned back to the chief and, pointing at the driver, said, "Look at Hassan here. He is from this area, like you. But he knows family planning and it has helped him with his life. Hasn't it, Hassan?"

"It has, Doctor, yes." Hassan nodded confidently. "Family planning is important."

"Right," Masoud said. "So, how many children do you have, Hassan?"

"Thirteen." Hassan's voice had lowered..

"Right... What?" Masoud turned to Hassan with astonishment. "You have thirteen kids?"

"No, just eight boys," Hassan said, "and four girls."

"Hassan!" Masoud said. "What about family planning, then?"

"I keep praying for less, but..."

The whole thing was awkward and funny for me at the same time. I was also wondering if, in their dialect, a 'kid' was a boy, or if they just didn't count their girls as kids.

On the way back that night, Hassan kept apologizing for embarrassing Masoud in front of the village people. "I should have lied," he kept saying. "I should have said I only have six children."

"Even six is too much, Hassan." Masoud was still frustrated. "And you shouldn't lie."

After a moment's pause, he continued, "Do you know how to use a condom?"

"Oh yes, of course." Hassan laughed.

"Then please don't have any more children," Masoud pleaded.

"I will try, Doctor," Hassan replied. "I will keep praying."

"Pray, sure, but also use a condom."

Alone with Masoud back at the *Seidoon* clinic, I noticed how he was visibly frustrated. We were getting ready to go to bed after an exhausting day. He was standing in front of the bathroom mirror, shaking his head.

"The driver, huh?" I asked.

"I just can't get to them," Masoud said. "They trust me when they're sick but, when it comes to their sex lives, the illiterate village Mullah is their ultimate authority."

"I'm already surprised they let you push for this sort of thing."

"Yeah, well, we're under pressure from the health ministry to reduce the birth rate." Masoud grabbed his toothbrush. "They've done well elsewhere. Only the *Seidoon* area and some place in the *Seestan* province have birth rates above four."

"Well, at least they're praying…" I was trying to be funny, but it was too late and we were too tired for humor.

"It's so frustrating." Masoud was brushing his teeth to the rhythm of the mourning chant playing from the *hosseinieh* loudspeaker.

***

The next morning, Masoud and I took the minibus back to *Baghmalek*. The plan was to spend a day there at the doctor's dorm where the ten or so medical draftees for the area shared a house. Some of the residents were stationed in *Baghmalek*, which was a four-fifth location on the draft duration scale. Others, like Masoud, occasionally stopped by and sometimes stayed the night there.

I already knew two or three of the doctors there, as they had gone to the same med school as Masoud, so we thought it would be fun to spend a night with them and play cards.

"We'll make *Seeraabi*!" Masoud, ever the consummate cook, had announced when we'd discussed the trip. I didn't particularly like *Seeraabi*, which was a stew consisting mainly of lamb intestines. The raw intestines stunk badly and so I did not trust it once it was cooked and stopped smelling so bad. But, if Masoud was cooking, it would likely taste fine.

We dumped our backpacks at the dorm house, visited the local grocery store, and on to the butchers to buy the lunch ingredients. There was no telephone in *Seidoon* or the dorm house, so we made sure we got enough change to last us a couple of calls and headed to the town's telephone center. Masoud called his parents, back in Tehran, and I called Dad in Ahwaz, mainly to tell him I was OK, and to confirm the time the next day when I'd be joining him at the airport to fly back home.

The cooking of the *Seeraabi* turned into a communal affair, with all five doctors at the dorm house pitching in to help Masoud. I, of course, did not have the least bit of interest in cooking, so I was tasked with setting the table.

Making the dish is not easy, and the doctors worked on it for quite a while, and everyone was starving by the time it was finally ready to eat.

"My God, this is tasty!" Mehdi, Masoud's friend from med school, said, slurping up the stew with his spoon.

"Umm! Delicious," Kazem, another one of the doctors, added. "Make sure you soak the bread in it." He cut bits of lavash bread into his bowl. "Leave it in for a few minutes."

"Heaven!" Masoud was smiling from ear to ear. "Best *Seeraabi* I've ever had."

After a moment of quiet indulgence, with everyone making happy eating sounds, someone asked me what I thought about *Baghmalek*.

"I like it," I answered. "Small, out of the way, and manageable. A far cry from Tehran's bustle."

"Ha! That's what we thought," Mehdi said, with the cup halfway to his mouth. "That feeling lasts for about two days."

"Then you realize there is pretty much nothing here to do and you're stuck," another doctor added.

"Some people like it here though," Kazem said.

"Like whom?" I asked.

"Like Doctor Naeeni." Everyone laughed at what was obviously an inside joke of theirs.

"He's a doctor with a private practice here," Masoud explained. "We don't like him much."

"Because he exploits the locals," Kazem said.

"Tell him about the sign outside his office," Mehdi said.

"Oh yeah!" Kazem laughed. "This guy is a hezbolahi and got accepted in the *Ezam* Konkoor." This was a nationwide exam to select students to send to overseas universities. "He goes to Romania and studies there for one term but gets homesick and returns. So, guess what his *Baghmalek* office sign says now?"

"What?" I chuckled in anticipation for the punchline.

"'Doctor Naeeni, with a Background in Research in Europe.'"

Everyone laughed.

"That's nothing," Mehdi said. "Did you guys hear about the doctor in *Izeh* who had a sign that read 'Doctor Raheemi, with Stethoscope from the U.S.'?"

Everyone laughed, but I didn't get the joke.

"A stethoscope," Masoud explained. "You know, the instrument doctors use to listen to your heart."

"Oh!" I laughed. "That can't be true though."

"I wouldn't be surprised," Masoud said. "People here are really gullible."

After lunch, we all sat around on the ground playing cards over who would clear the table and wash the dishes.

"That *Seeraabi* was good, man," said one of the doctors.

Mehdi let out a slight burp. "Excuse me. Yeah, I am so full I can't move."

"By the way," Masoud said, putting a bowl of sunflower seeds on the ground for everyone to share. "You washed it clean like I said, right?"

After a moment's silence, Mehdi said, "You're asking me?"

"Yeah. Weren't you tasked with cleaning the intestine when we got home?"

"Not me," Mehdi replied. "I thought Kazem was to do it. I chopped the garlic."

"I cleaned the herbs," Kazem said. "I thought you were cleaning the intestines."

Everyone stared at each other trying to remember what had happened.

"I did notice some green stuff in the stew," I said. "I thought it was part of the dish. It must have been…"

"Ewww!" Kazem cried.

Masoud fake threw up. Mehdi held his hand on his mouth, and I said what everyone was thinking: "We all just ate sheep poo!"

What a commotion! Masoud started fake strangling Mehdi, as another one of the doctors fake beat-up Kazem, and I quickly peeked at Masoud's cards, so he turned to clobber me, and Mehdi emptied the cup of sunflower seeds on him, and the chaos went on for another five minutes before we all lay on the ground panting.

"Well," Masoud announced, finally. "Now we know the secret to making the most delicious *Seeraabi* ever!"

"Ewww!" everyone cried again, in unison.

***

That night, Masoud, Mehdi, Kazem, and I shared a room with two bunk beds. It turned out that Kazem had also been a fellow student at Masoud's med school, but I had never met him before.

"Actually," Masoud remembered, "Kazem is originally from *Seidoon*."

"Really?" I asked. "You grew up here?"

"Yeah." Kazem smiled.

"Wow!" I said. "Must be great to be serving your birthplace."

"It's OK," Kazem replied.

"Are you going to set up a private practice here once you're done with the service?" I asked.

"Not really. I really don't like it here much."

"So, what's the plan?"

"I'm leaving."

"The country?" I was surprised.

Kazem nodded. "If I can, yeah."

"But why?" I asked.

"He wants to get his PhD," Masoud answered for him. "Kazem is a genius. He'll find the cure for cancer someday. Just wait."

Kazem laughed. "Well, if not cancer, at least I'll cure my boredom."

"But how is this country ever going to improve if our best and brightest keep leaving?" I asked. I knew I was being inconsiderate, but I couldn't help myself.

"This country is hopeless," Kazem said. "I grew up in *Seidoon*, yes, and went to elementary school there. Most kids quit school after fifth grade. You know what happens to those who want to continue?"

I shook my head.

"They have to come to *Baghmalek* for high school. And then, if they are top of class and study hard, they pass the Konkoor, and where do they end up? The nearest university is in Ahwaz, where your dads teach."

"You're literally drained away," I said.

"Every once in a while, against all odds, someone gets such high marks in the Konkoor that they end up in Tehran, and discover that there's a big, exciting, happening world out there." He was obviously talking about himself. "Why would he ever want to go back?"

"I guess."

"It's true, city boy," he said, smiling. "You grew up in it, so you take it for granted."

"It's like evolution," Masoud added. "Only in reverse."

We all fell silent, thinking about it for a while as we lay in our bunk beds. Kazem had painted a disturbing image in my brain of what was happening to Iran. What was happening to the world, really? *Why is this thing set up this way?* I thought. *This can't be the natural order of things.*

But then, the images of my short trip to *Seidoon* started flooding my brain. The ladies washing the dishes. The young volunteers at the House of Healthcare. I saw the ambulance driver in my mind's eye and realized that he was only being polite with his refrain of promising to pray. I saw the village chief and remembered how he was proud in the face of being patronized by Masoud. I saw the pride in the rhythmic dance of the barleys forming those violent waves. I saw the teenage girl in her full ethnic regalia, and in my mind, I got to look her in the eyes, and this time, I saw confidence. I saw calm. She was fine. They were fine.

"Masoud," I whispered. "Are you awake?"

"Yeah."

"Evolution can't run in reverse," I said.

He thought about it.

"I mean, these folks are OK here."

"No, they're not."

"I mean, you and I think they're not, and that's why we won't be living here," I said. "But…"

"You think they wouldn't leave if they could?" Masoud asked, teasingly.

"Well…" I really didn't know. "I guess if they could. If they knew, they would be different people, wouldn't they? And then they wouldn't fit here that easily anymore."

"Like we don't fit here."

"Yeah. I guess." I was no longer quite sure what we were talking about.

"Pray for them," Masoud said, with a snicker.

I tried gathering my thoughts to argue with him, but I was too tired to talk. I had a big day of traveling ahead tomorrow, and a bunch of computer programming work to catch up on the day after. This whole trip would feel like a distant memory by then. Like a dream. I shut my eyes and fell asleep.

THE RALLY

"*G*o, Babak," Arash Azami said on the phone, "you got that programmable calculator, right?"

"Yeah...?"

"You know how to program, right?"

As an engineering student, I had recently signed up and won a government-subsidized programmable calculator, which I had bragged about to Arash, who was studying medicine and wasn't eligible for one.

"Sort of."

"What do you mean 'sort of'?" Arash asked. "I thought you just got your master's in software engineering. You forgot already?"

"No." I chuckled. "Anyway, you can't have it. You'll break it."

"Yeah, I guess I'll have to get you to go with it too, don't I?"

"Where? You planning to enter all those disease names you have to memorize into its memory to cheat on your exams? It only has two kilobytes, you know."

"No, no, no. You heard about the Tehran Rally?"

"Yeah." I'd seen something in the newspaper.

"Well, my friends and I are entering, and we need a calculator."

211

"Cool! Count me in."

It was the early '90s, and I had a lot of time on my hands, being in an in-between time of having just gotten my master's and waiting to be drafted (for a second time). The war had been over for a few years now and we were well into Rafsanjani's era of 'Reconstruction.' The economy was booming, and the government was loosening its reigns on social freedoms ever so slightly. The Automobile and Racing Federation had reopened recently, and they were heavily promoting their first 'Family' Rally, to help portray car-racing in a positive light, justifying their existence as a means to promoting safe and good driving habits rather than a decadent rich man's sport.

None of us had cars back then, even second-hand cars were too expensive to own, so when not using taxis, we relied on our parents' generosity to get around town. My dad had a Nissan Datsun from way back before the revolution, and it was the family workhorse. There was no way he'd allow me to enter a rally with it, so the thought hadn't even occurred to me. Arash's university friend, Navid, though, had secured permission to enter the race with his dad's old Peugeot 504. He'd asked Arash to join him as navigator, and another one of his friends as the second driver. Each team was allowed up to four members, but only two drivers could sign up per team.

I got to work, learning how to code the little device, and wrote some code to help with the rally. Arash had given me the rally's sample navigation instructions to work off of. This was a little leaflet that gave us a starting point and clues as to how to get to each waypoint to the sample finish-line. The idea was that we had to be able to follow the map clues correctly and not get lost. We also had clue-like instructions as to the expected duration between each waypoint, and points were deducted for getting there too early or too late. The program I was writing was supposed to be able to take any clues available and help us adjust our speed by entering the car's odometer reading along the way.

A few days before the race, the four of us went to the Fereshteh neighborhood of uptown Tehran to try out the sample route. That's where I met Navid, the driver, and his scruffy-looking friend, Reza, for the first time. Arash, Navid, and Reza were all third-year medical students at the same university.

Tehran is essentially a great big sprawl that, over a period of a hundred years, grew at an astoundingly rapid pace from a little village of a few hundred people to a massive twelve million-strong capital. There was no urban planning involved, and as it grew, it ended up swallowing all of the neighboring villages. The Fereshteh area was one such neighborhood, consisting of a mesh of narrow streets, twisting and turning and conspiring to confuse the poor uninformed driver. Most of us had practiced driving there with our parents at one time or other, and once, Kaivan had famously found himself at an intersection on a one-way road with all three outlets being one-ways against him. He had called it the Fereshteh Vortex: a scheme by the Tehran traffic police to reduce the number of cars on the streets.

"It's like a black hole," he'd explained. "No getting out when you fall into it."

Sure enough, on the day of the practice, we got lost quite a few times, and navigational troubles foreshadowed the use of my program: there was really little use for knowing your desired speed when you weren't on the correct path in the first place. It didn't help that we kept running into other, equally confused, rally participants, driving in the opposite direction or taking a different turn from what we thought the clues were obviously telling us.

"We're pathetic," Navid declared. He seemed to be the pessimistic type.

"It wasn't that bad," I objected. "We did make it to the finish line."

"We think we made it to the finish line," he corrected me.

"I think it was the finish line," Arash said, confidently. "I think the red VW was wrong to turn off at the earlier intersection."

"I bet she thinks the same of us," Navid said. "We're not even sure if the start point was right."

"My program didn't crash," I said.

"We're pathetic," Navid said again, making me wonder how he'd brought himself to form this team and enter in the race in the first place.

***

I got up very early on the morning of the rally and made my way down to Azadi Square, where Navid was to pick us up. Arash was already there, and Reza showed up a little later, but there was no sign of Navid.

"You sure you told him the time, right?" I asked Arash.

"He said six a.m. himself."

"Why so early anyway, the race won't start till eight?" Reza asked.

Arash shrugged.

"Did he say Azadi? Maybe he's waiting for us at the highway toll booths?" I asked.

"No, he said Azadi."

"That's stupid though, why not at the highway? This isn't even on his way."

Arash shrugged again. "Did you bring the calculator?"

I took the device out of my pocket and waved it at him.

"Did you fix your code?"

"There's nothing wrong with my code," I objected.

"It was useless on our test run."

"Your brain-code is useless. Did you learn how to navigate yet?"

"Is that him?" Reza pointed at a Peugeot turning around the square.

"That's not him," Arash said.

"Did you guys remember to bring your driver's licenses?"

"Shoot!" Reza said. "Do we need that?"

"Of course, you need that, mister-second-driver, how else are you gonna register?"

"Shoot," Reza said again, wide-eyed. "I'll go grab it."

"Too late, man." Arash shook his head. "That's OK. You can help with the navigation."

"That's right," I said. "We need a good navigator anyway."

Arash gave me a mock glare, and Reza laughed.

Arash Azami was an 'Ahwazi' friend. Our parents were university professors and we went way back to the pre-war years when we all lived on the university campus we called the Kooy. Our friendship was special, and our constant bickering was part of announcing to the world that we were so close we could actually be totally rude to one another and it wouldn't even matter. It was funny, and sometimes, it could be hurtful too, but we didn't really let it get to us for long.

Arash's parents had emigrated to Australia right after he'd passed the nation-wide university entrance exam and got into med school. I never completely figured out why they did it. I guess, by Western standards he'd been old enough to be independent and should have been thankful for the house they left behind for him, but in Iran, kids typically stayed with their parents, sometimes well into their twenties, while they went to college and until they found a job.

"Where the heck is this friend of yours anyway?" I asked him.

"I'll go call him," Arash said. "Maybe his alarm clock didn't work." And he went to find a pay phone.

"Did he have the nightshift or something?" I asked Reza.

"That's for interns," he explained. "We're not there yet."

I really didn't have much to say to Reza. "Do you guys call each other 'Doctor' at school yet? Like 'Doctor Azami'?"

Reza looked at me proudly. "We'll get to do that once we take the Hippocratic Oath."

"Hmm, I always got a kick out of how the med students called each other 'doctor' at boot camp when we got drafted as students," I said. "So, I guess they weren't supposed to be doing that yet."

A few minutes of awkward silence between me and Reza as we scanned the traffic before Arash showed up.

"Domestic issues," he called out as he neared us.

"What do you mean?"

"His dad is having second thoughts about the car."

"What?"

"Couldn't he have sneaked out without waking his dad up?" Reza asked.

"Anyway, looks like it's resolved," Arash said. "He should be here soon."

Navid did arrive shortly thereafter, but by the time we finally got to the rally sign-in, we were one of the last cars in the line to get our number. Every car was handed three cool-looking, large, glossy, sticky papers with their number in big red digits printed on them, and they stuck them on the sides and on the front hood.

"Look at that!" I pointed at a Renault 5 full of pretty girls with colorful scarfs that already had its number sticker on. "I wish I had your numbers!" I called out, and the girls giggled. "Looks just like a real sports car."

By the time we got to the registration booth, though, they had run out of the sticker numbers.

"We're really sorry," the federation official said. "We've been overwhelmed by the number of show-ups. We only had a hundred printed sticker numbers. Please write your numbers on these papers and stick them on with the paper-tape."

"What the heck?" Arash complained.

"We would probably have gotten a single digit sticker had someone not been late," said Reza.

"Hey, let's make the most of it," Arash said. "Who's got the best handwriting?"

So, Reza ended up drawing a pretty good italicized One Hundred and Three on all three pieces of A4 paper, and we stuck them on the car with the paper-tape. It looked clunky. So much for looking cool with a numbered rally car.

The cars lined up in order and every thirty seconds, the next car would be flagged to the starting line, receive the navigation instructions to the next station, after which it would be signaled to start the race.

Navid was at the wheel with Arash, the navigator, sitting next to him. I was sitting behind the driver so I could read the odometer over his shoulder. We were all pretty excited, waiting our turn. I started practicing using my calculator, and I guess that was getting on Arash's nerves.

"Don't waste the battery, dude."

"It's solar," I replied.

"Doesn't it have battery back-up?"

"Nope."

"What if there's an eclipse?"

"Then I wouldn't be able to read the numbers anyway, you moron."

After a brief silence and me punching more numbers in, Arash turned to me. "Can you just put that thing away? It's getting on my nerves. Plus, you might screw up the program… I don't know… accidentally erase it or something."

"It's not in program mode."

"Whatever, just…"

I put the calculator in my pocket. "OK, OK."

"Remember," the start line official said when it was our turn, "breaking traffic rules is an immediate disqualification and going too fast will cost you points. Drive safely. Here you go." he handed Arash the navigation instructions.

I looked at the odometer and typed it into the calculator. "Distance?" I asked Arash.

"Doesn't say," Arash replied. "Go straight at speed limit."

"What's the speed limit?"

"Must be twenty-five out here," Reza said.

"But the car before us was doing sixty at least," said Navid.

"So, what's the distance then?" I was getting annoyed.

"Go twenty-five," Arash said to Navid. "They said we should go at speed limit if there's no other info."

"I'll do thirty, just in case." Navid accelerated a bit.

"Do we have a distance?" I called.

Arash lost it. "No, goddamn it! We don't have a freakin' distance, OK?"

I looked over Arash's shoulder. "What's that little number on the bottom left side of the map?"

"This?"

"Yeah, isn't that distance?"

"Says 'one.' I thought that was the map number."

"Doesn't say 'two' on the second map though, does it?"

"Hmm, must be one kilometer then."

"Great," I murmured, as I punched the distance into the calculator. "We got a dyslexic for a navigator."

"I think you need to turn here," Reza said. We were still on the boulevard heading north from the stadium. All the intersections looked the same here, in the undeveloped part of what used to be the outskirts of Tehran. "No, wait…!" Arash stared intently at the directions. "That was the turn-off we just passed, and the light is up there on the next block, so… yeah, turn here."

Navid made a sharp right-turn.

"Um, it was pretty obvious," Reza said.

"How did you know so fast?" Arash asked.

"The car in front of us turned here."

Arash looked ahead to the numbered car in the distance. "Oh. Right." Then he shrugged it off. "Well, they may be making a mistake. We should do our own calculations." He looked at the next map.

"We're pathetic—" Navid said, but he was interrupted by Arash.

"Don't start that now."

Each map or direction seemed to have a little riddle in it. At first glance, they seemed to be missing some information, but an hour or so into it, we started getting the hang of it, and we were making good progress. We did make a few mistakes, but they weren't huge and nothing a quick U-turn or speed adjustment wouldn't rectify.

We were all so busy with the navigation that we hardly noticed the passage of time and the transition through the neighborhoods. The course took us from the starting line at Azadi Stadium west of town, to the back streets of the new Ziba-Shahr neighborhood, where the extent of Tehran's sprawl had reached, on to Aryashahr, near Masoud's place, for whom I was registering much of what was happening so I could tell him when we next met, through the hills of Evin, around the dreaded prison, up to steep uptown Velenjak, where my Uncle Kourosh lived.

We twisted and turned a lot through the streets of Velenjak, always moving up. It seemed like the directions were pushing us to climb up the mountain and indeed, before long, we found ourselves at the very end of Velenjak Street and at the entrance to the Tochal Mountain Climbing and Recreational Area, where we stopped at the next rally checkpoint. We handed our rally stamp book to the race official, who stamped it and tore off a stub.

"Are we winning?" I asked through Navid's window.

The guy chuckled. "Of course, you are winning," he said, sarcastically. "Now don't forget: breaking traffic rules is an immediate disqualification and going too fast will cost you points. Drive safely. Here you go." He handed us the next direction booklet.

"Wasn't this the same guy as the one at the starting point?" I asked.

"Looked the same, didn't he?" asked Navid.

The directions called for us to go straight down Velenjak, probably the steepest street in Tehran. At the very bottom, there was a wall, into which, just last year, a minibus of schoolchildren had crashed and killed all twenty kids and the driver. This was fresh on our minds as we zoomed down at the calculator's suggested sixty kilometers per hour speed.

"Shoot! The brake's not working." Navid held the steering wheel tight with both hands.

"Stop it!" Arash retorted.

"I'm not kidding!"

The car filled with the smell of burning brake pads.

"Pull the hand-brake!" Reza said.

"No," I said. "You need to slow it down more for that. Can you gear it down?"

"Dude, I won't disengage the clutch without a brake!"

"Is it emptied out?" Arash asked.

"Yeah, it's flooring."

This was getting scarier by the heartbeat.

"Just press it down repeatedly, it'll pump in more brake fluid," Arash said.

The car started slowing down a bit, and Navid shifted down, until we came to a full stop, a few yards from the wall.

We sat there silent for a while. I had cold sweat on the back of my neck and my knees were shaking. We were half-stunned, half-thinking what to do next.

Reza broke the silence. "Whew! That was close."

"No shit!" Arash said, beads of sweat coming down his forehead.

"What do we do now?" Reza asked.

"We'd have to drive at ninety kilometers per hour if we want to make up for the time," I joked, looking at the calculator.

"I guess that's the end of the race," Reza said.

"My dad's not gonna like this." Navid shook his head.

"Can you drive it in first gear?" Arash asked.

"Yeah," Navid replied. "You're not thinking of continuing the race in first gear, are you?"

"Sure I am," answered Arash.

"You're nuts," I said.

"No I'm not."

"Just let me out here. I'll catch a cab home," said Reza.

"Wait!" Arash said suddenly. "Hear me out. I've got an idea."

I sighed. "I don't like it already."

"We drive down to my place and switch to my car," said Arash.

"What, the Paykan?"

"Yeah, why not?"

Arash's parents had left him their old fridge-white Paykan, the ubiquitous Hillman knock-off made in Iran. That car had had many mechanical issues, and Arash didn't really drive it around much anymore, preferring to take public transport instead.

"Didn't they say there can only be two drivers per car?" I asked.

"Yeah, but we can change the designation if we change the car," Arash said.

"Where the heck does it say *that* in the rules?"

"Where the heck does it say we can change cars?" Reza pointed out, silencing the debate again.

"Come on!" Arash said. "What's life without a little mischief? I mean, we're breaking the law every day just simply by existing in this Islamic Republic. Let's do it!"

That pretty much made the decision for us.

So, we drove a good two miles, all in first gear, down to Arash's place. By the time we got there, Navid's car wouldn't stop without the handbrake, which was also starting to smell funny.

"My dad's not gonna like this," Navid said again after we got out of the car and he locked it up.

We then got to work on Arash's Paykan, which was so dirty the numbers we'd carefully peeled off of the Peugeot would simply not stick onto its body.

We found a rag in his trunk and wiped the dirt off the three areas we needed cleaned. Arash then took the driver's seat, and Reza switched in as the navigator. Navid sat in the back with me, staring sadly at his car as we whizzed away.

"We're off course and very late," Reza said. "Let's get back to Velenjak as soon as possible and continue where we left off."

"No," Arash replied, "we don't need to. The directions are pretty simple. We need to get ourselves to Gisha Bridge."

"You sure your brakes are good?" I asked, after Arash made a couple of sharp turns and started speeding on the parkway. But there was really not much room for joking at that moment. Everyone was frowning and staring ahead with intent.

We made the five-mile trip in a whopping four minutes, with Arash driving like a cabbie, zigzagging part of the way through alleyways while we all held on for dear life.

"Which panel are we continuing from?" Reza asked. He had been flipping through the pages frantically all along and had finally brought himself to admit his confusion.

"Should be the third or fourth one on the second page," replied Arash.

Reza was still confused, frowning and rotating the page this way and that.

"Let me see." I snatched it out of his hands and looked at it for a moment. "It's that one." I pointed. "That's the bridge. We're headed that way."

I punched in the odometer reading on my calculator as soon as we got back on track. "… two, two forty-three, zero five two…" I read out loud. "Let me know as soon as we get to the next panel, Reza."

But Reza looked lost again, and I had to point it out to him. "There— it's right when we turn on to Gisha."

"Which one is Gisha again?" Reza asked.

"This one!" Arash made a sudden turn onto the main street.

"Darn you, Arash!" I picked the calculator off the floor. "Read me the damn odometer!"

"Fifty-two…" Arash read.

"Shoot!" I said. "What's that again?"

"Five. Two," he replied.

"I keep getting a division-by-zero," I said.

Arash sighed. "I knew I couldn't count on you to write a simple program without bugs."

"Just read me the damned odometer," I growled.

"Two hundred, twenty-four thousand, fifty-two," he read, with considerable annoyance.

"Darn!" It wasn't working. "Maybe you broke my calculator with your crazy driving."

"Where do I go now?" Arash asked Reza, who was sweating and rotating the navigation instructions left and right again, trying to decipher it.

I looked over his hand. "Looks like you need to make a U-turn at the light."

I pressed a few buttons and checked the code in programming mode, and it all seemed to be fine. Arash made the U-turn and called out the odometer reading again. "Fifty-two!"

"What?"

"I said, fifty-two!"

"I heard you." I looked over his shoulder and sure enough, the digits had not changed. "Your fuckin' odometer is broken, you idiot!"

"What?" Arash checked. "I guess you're right." He grinned widely.

"Of course I'm right." I laughed. "Either that or we're lost in space-time too."

"So what do I do?" Arash asked.

"Um," Reza said, "I'm not sure."

Navid broke his silence. "Let's just quit and go home." He sounded very depressed.

Arash made a sudden swerve to the right and stopped the car.

"You know what?" He turned to face us. "Anyone who wants to quit can leave now. I wanna finish this."

We all looked at him. I'd rarely seen him so serious.

"Anyone?"

But we just sat there looking at him.

"OK, then." He turned to Reza. "Reza-jaan, why don't you take a

221

break and change with Babak?"

I jumped out of the car and handed Reza the calculator as I went by him to sit in the front.

"What do I do with this?" he asked.

"I don't know," I said. "Program it."

***

From there on, with the competition's intensity all but gone for us, the race became much more fun. We had time to talk and enjoy the route, and even poked fun at some of the other cars that were lost, or were going super-slow or way too fast, trying to get back on the race time. Arash and I were less snippy at each other, or maybe the snipes hurt less and so were funnier now. At one point, both Reza and Navid fell asleep in the back and we riffed off of each other talking about their 'incredible level of excitement' for the rally.

The end of the race was an anti-climactic affair. We were exhausted and by then the whole thing had become rather tedious. There seemed to be no more riddles in the navigation instructions and the organizers seemed to have just filled the last few pages by trying to tire us down and confuse us in the dirt roads north of the stadium, before bringing us in to the finish line.

"What? No checkered flag?" I said when we approached the last stop-point.

The official, who we were pretty sure by now was the same guy on the first two checkpoints, reached out and took the book from Arash and stamped it.

"So… did we win?" Arash asked him, sarcastically.

"Results will be announced in a ceremony at Laleh Hotel next month," he said, mechanically. "Thank you and drive safely." He waved us on.

***

I had a shaved head when I met my team members at the Laleh Hotel reception a few weeks later. I'd just been assigned the police force for my second draft, and I was to report to Parandak boot camp, thirty miles south-west of Tehran. This was my last day of freedom.

"Hah!" Arash pointed at my head as soon as he saw me. "I thought you went through that once already?" He was referring to my six-month student draft from a few years ago.

"Yeah, sucks," I mumbled.

"That boot camp didn't count?"

"Only if I'd ended up in the air force again." I smiled. "But I'll be a police officer! Just what I wanted when I was a kid."

"Yeah," Arash said. "Being a policeman in a police state isn't as cool though, is it?"

"It's got its perks," I replied. "I can pick on girls and ask them to straighten their hijab and wipe their make-up off."

"You might as well," Arash said. "With that head, you don't have any other chance a girl would take you seriously anyway."

That made me blush, as I'd been eyeing the pretty girls at the ceremony, marveling at the fact that it looked like we would be able to sit next to them, given there didn't seem to be any designated gender-specific seating going on.

"I guess you can do that now if it's considered a family event." Arash was reading my mind.

"Cool!" I said.

"Dude, sit somewhere else and pretend you don't know me," Arash said. "No chance of me picking up a girl with you around."

He was joking, of course, and we did sit as a group.

There was, as is usually the case with such ceremonies, a long and boring intro with a lot of thanking people, and thanking each other, and thanking us. The organizers were genuinely amazed and very happy with the fact that they'd been able to pull the event off with no disturbance from the authorities.

They then showed a short video compilation from the event, with some funny moments of cars being lost, drivers being confused, or people going very, *very* slow, pulling up to a stop point in order to make it there at the exact right time.

"They completely edited us out, didn't they?" I asked.

"Better," Reza said. "We'd get disqualified if they noticed we switched cars."

The MC went back on stage. "There were one hundred and twenty sign-ups for the rally," he started. "I'm happy to say that an unprecedented sixty-five cars actually completed the race."

"What does he mean, 'unprecedented'?" I whispered. "Isn't this the first rally we've ever had?"

"Shh! Let him use his big words," Arash said.

"As for those who completed the race…" the MC went on, "I will read the names and numbers of the drivers in reverse order, starting from sixty-fifth."

"Great! We'll know our rank before most other people here," Arash said, and got some chuckles from a few people sitting near us.

The MC read through the names from number sixty-five to fifty. With every name, a bunch of people cheered and most of us clapped, which was another newfound liberty for us: a few short years back, clapping would have been frowned upon and the preferred cheer was to praise the prophet Mohammad and his family, in Arabic.

"Wow!" I couldn't believe it. "We're better than fiftieth place. That's pretty good."

"Shh!" Arash said. "Was that our name?"

"No," Navid replied. "Some folks cheered over there."

We were not in the list of rank fifty to forty, either. Nor forty to thirty.

"I'm sure he read our names already," Said Arash.

Reza shook his head. "I don't think so."

"I'm pretty sure we were disqualified," Navid said. "He said half the entrants never finished the race, remember? He didn't say why. Maybe the disqualified were bundled in that number."

"But we did finish the race," I argued, as the MC started reading numbers thirty to twenty. "Wouldn't they have told us at the end of the race if we'd been disqualified?"

Arash shrugged. "Maybe they found out later, when they were editing the video." He looked at me with a smile.

"Shh!" It was my turn to shush him.

Incredibly, our name was not read up until rank ten, at which point the MC paused for three trophy cups to be carried in, along with a bunch of rolled up glossy papers tied with red ribbons, all neatly laid out on the table before him.

"From here on, I'd like the teams I call to come up to the podium please," the MC said.

"Let's go home and save ourselves the embarrassment," Arash said. "There's no way we're in the top ten."

"I'm surprised you thought we'd even be ranked," said Navid.

"Wishing is no vice for the youth," Reza quoted.

By the time the tenth to third places were announced, I was certain that our name would not be read that day. I was quite disappointed and even had a little lump in my throat; I wanted this to turn into a story to tell: 'we goofed up all along and still came in twenty-third'—something like that. But the reality, as always, seemed to be harsher. The organizers had found us out and disqualified us, or worse yet, they had misplaced our records and we'd simply walk away from here with an apology. 'We are terribly sorry guys, we're not sure how this happened. We hope you had fun anyway.' That's all I'd take with me to the scary unknown of the police force boot camp tomorrow.

Hands in my pockets, I had slumped down on my seat with my eyes glazed over, feeling sorry for myself, when I was nudged by Arash.

"They called our name!" he was saying.

I looked at him like I'd just woken up.

"Get up!" He nudged me again.

In a daze, I made my way up to the podium, following Arash, Navid, and Reza, shaking a few hands, and lifting the second-place trophy to some pretty loud applause.

***

Arash ended up taking the cup home, Navid got the diploma and a cut of the prize money, which he shared with Reza. My booty was a clunky car stereo from one of the sponsors. It was worse than the one we already had in our old Nissan Datsun, but I installed it anyway, thinking it would end up being a good excuse for telling the story behind how I got it. Our names got printed in the newspaper and we enjoyed some minor celebrity amongst friends for a few days.

Masoud, Siamak, Kaivan, and I entered the rally again the following year and came in thirty-seventh; only ten behind Arash's team.

LEAVING HOME

" *W*ill you go, Mr. Hodjat?"
Well, of course not. Of that I was certain.

I'd been in a state of uncertainty since finishing my military service the year before. I'd sent out applications to a number of universities and I'd gotten a few acceptances, but I didn't have the money to pay for the tuition and I didn't want to take any more of my parents' money. I flew out to the UK and met a professor that expressed a lot of interest in having me be his student. I wanted to find out if he'd give me a job at his lab, but budgets were tight, and nothing had come out of it. I'd taken the nationwide overseas scholarship exam reluctantly, knowing I'd never again take money from the Iranian government. I didn't want any more obligations.

I finally got a letter from my buddy at the University of Southern California, USC. He'd been a couple of years my senior in undergrad and had skipped military service to go to the US. He was a smart kid and was faculty now, so he'd gotten me in. That was it then! I was coming to the US.

I got a pretty good score on my government scholarship exam and followed the process just to hedge my chances in case the USC thing fell through. I'd been awarded an Iranian government scholarship to go to

227

Japan, and that amused me. I knew nothing about Japan, and it was the last place I'd ever imagined going. Even so, after buying my tickets and arranging to get my student visa at the US Embassy in Turkey on my way to L.A., I still continued with the process, more out of curiosity now than anything else.

As the last step, I was to hand in some documents at the Japanese Embassy. I'd been inside once for the interviews but, this time, I was simply to meet the Iranian admin in the waiting area outside.

"So, will you go, Mr. Hodjat?" she asked me casually as she checked the papers. She was around my own age, with a long and pretty face, walnut eyes, curved brows, and long hair—one of the perks of working at an embassy in Iran: no need for a hijab.

We were standing in the empty lobby area, before security checks. They didn't let people into the building unless they absolutely needed to.

"No," I said, quite honestly.

"No?" She looked surprised. "But why not?"

"I don't want to owe the government anything," I replied.

"Ok…" she said.

"Plus," I added, with a smile, "I don't want to get married."

She looked at me, a bit confused. She was pretty and maybe she thought I was flirting with her. And maybe I was.

"It's the law. If I accept this scholarship I'd have to be married when I get on the plane to Japan."

"Really?"

"Too many people have never come back." I laughed. "It's the mullahs' convoluted solution to the brain-drain problem."

She laughed. "That's a pity. You have a strong case." She pointed at the documents.

I thanked her and left, wondering about her last comment. I'd thought of her as an admin, but by the next day, it became clear to me that she had a bigger role at the embassy than I'd expected.

"Hello?"

It was her.

"Yes?"

"Mr. Hodjat, can you come to the Japanese Embassy today?"

"Today?"

"Yes; it's about our little discussion yesterday."

"Sure."

At first, I thought maybe they were going to reject my application, but then, why would they ask me to the embassy for that?

I was led into the office area by the admin where I was introduced to a middle-aged Japanese man in a suit and tie, Mr. Yamamoto, the educational attaché.

"How do you do, Mr. Hodjat?" he asked, very officially, after we shook hands. He offered me to sit down on the couch in front of him, and the admin took the seat right next to him, smiling, as if to say 'See? I'm more important than you thought.'

We sat there for a few minutes in silence, as he paged through my file.

"Mr. Hodjat," he finally said, still looking at the papers, "you have a very strong file."

"Thank you." I was still not sure what that meant.

"We would like for you to continue your studies in Japan." He looked at me sternly. He looked back down at the files again and continued in a lower tone, "But I've heard that you have decided not to go?"

"Well…" I looked at the admin, and she seemed to be nodding me on. "Yes, it is very unlikely that I would go."

The official pretended to be reviewing the file some more. "May I ask the reason?"

"The main reason is that I do not want to get married." I explained the ridiculous law, and the fact that I wanted to concentrate on my studies and marriage would be a huge distraction. I did also mention my misgivings about obligations to the Ministry of Higher Education to work at a government-assigned job when I was back.

Mr. Yamamoto nodded and paged through the papers some more. I began to wonder why I was being interrogated like this and started feeling a bit uncomfortable. I wasn't doing anything illegal, was I?

He finally looked up at me and declared, "Mr. Hodjat, should the Japanese government give you a no-obligation, full-ride scholarship, independent from the Iranian government, would you accept?"

I was surprised. I was not expecting this at all. I mumbled a bit, saying I wasn't sure what that meant. He started enumerating the benefits of the Monbusho Scholarship and how it was a privilege given to a select few, but I was only half-listening. A file, long closed and stored in my brain, on the whole decision as to where to go and what to do next in my life, was being retrieved from the vaults, but my mind had been made up already.

It was hard to say no to the guy's face, so I asked him for some time to decide.

"OK. But I will need to know in the next few days," he said. "Would you please call me with your decision before the end of the week?"

***

During the next few days, I gradually warmed up to the idea. I didn't know anything about Japan. A new country, a new culture, a new language. I did know a Japanese professor, though, with whom I had been exchanging emails regarding my research. I sent him an email explaining the situation and asking if he'd be willing to take me as a student under the Monbusho Scholarship. I got a quick reply that very night that he would. The stars seemed to be aligning. No obligations, a fully paid scholarship, no risk of a rejected visa, the professor I knew, Japan's five-year plan to promote AI research... I also liked the fact that the embassy folks had made an exception in my case. It made me feel special.

Most importantly, it was the kind of surprise, last-minute, life-changing decision I liked to make. It fit my profile. It fit my story.

I accepted the offer.

***

I met love on the phone.

I've always been in love. Almost always. Ever since I remember. Ever since Miss Meyers in kindergarten. But this was real, and powerful, and unlike anything I'd ever experienced before, and I sensed it barely five minutes into the phone call.

It was a week before the Persian New Year, Norooz. I had just gotten back home from my last day of work and I was sitting at the desk next to my brother, Siamak, waiting my turn to play Leisure Suit Larry on the desktop.

I felt light. I was done with all my obligations. No more responsibilities. Just, enjoy life for the next three weeks, before flying abroad for my new life as a PhD student.

And then the phone rang.

"It's for you," my dad said, and I picked up the phone next to the computer.

Her velvety voice was a bit deep. She sounded confident. She sounded smart–funny. She was honest, while remaining mysterious. I started feeling like I really wanted to meet her. It was too soon for that–we'd only talked for five minutes. It was too late for that–I was about to leave the country in three weeks.

"Please don't make me fall in love with you. I don't have the time," I joked.

We talked for more than an hour.

It was common in those days for young folks to make anonymous calls to strangers. It was an exciting game, and phone numbers of boys or girls who were 'fun to talk to' would go hand in hand. The calls were usually kept anonymous and there was no obligation to continue talking. If you got bored, you just hung up, pretty much mid-sentence, and they would usually never call again.

The voice on the other end said she had called because she had been hurt by a friend she highly respected, and she'd been depressed, and someone who knew me had given her my number, saying I'd cheer her up. She was a high school literature teacher. The way she described what she did in class reminded me of the movie *Dead Poets Society*. She had 'fallen' a few years ago. I didn't understand what she meant by that, but it had changed her. It had changed her life. Her words sang to me in a beautiful, elaborate rhythm, almost musical. This is what inspires beautiful poetry. It is poetry. Delicately precious poetry.

I walked in a semi-daze for the rest of the day. It was almost as if I was longing to hear her lovely voice again from the moment we hung up. I didn't want to do anything, but I couldn't sit still either. I just wanted to think about her, and I did my best thinking when I walked, so I went for a long walk, up next to the river for miles, all the way from Zafar to Tajrish. Thinking.

***

She called a few more times and we finally decided to meet near the modern arts museum.

After a good half hour of prep, fussing over what to wear in order to look casual, I took a cab down to Laleh Park. She had told me the make and model of her car, and I waited on the sidewalk looking for a light-blue Renault 5, wishing with all my might that she not be too ugly.

Ten minutes or so later, I spotted the car parallel parking a few yards up the street, and I caught a glimpse of her face. Framed by the dark blue veil was the most beautiful face I'd ever seen. Indescribably beautiful. (So pretty, I struggled that night to remember it. I think my brain was too afraid to make a mistake in reconstructing it, so it wasn't even trying.)

She's pretty! I thought, completely elated. *She's the nicest voice in the world, and she's pretty!*

"Hi." I greeted her with a handshake once she got out of the car. "I'm Babak. Well done on the parallel parking."

"Hello, I'm Jila." She smiled and her radiant smile just melted my soul. I had never felt anything like it.

The museum was closed. We took a quick stroll through the park, but it was not safe for a young man and woman who were unrelated to be walking around. The revolutionary guards might pick on us.

"Let's go to my place," I insisted. I wanted us to be in a safe environment. I think she realized that, but she was still apprehensive.

"I won't come alone. Let's go pick up my friend. She lives near your neighborhood."

Her friend was funny and more talkative than her. I felt like she had tasked herself with measuring me up. She was working her way up to a verdict she'd announce to Jila later in a long, private girly conversation reviewing the day's events.

Siamak and Kaivan were at our place when we got there. I introduced them to my new friends, and we played cards. I know it sounds silly, but I really didn't like sitting around and chitchatting, and I loved playing games, and so did my friends.

As it turned out, lovely Jila and her friend didn't mind it either. Nor did they find it particularly surprising or offending that we should sit down to a game of cards even before having been introduced properly.

***

On the first day, we talked. On the second day, we met. On the third day, we kissed. On the fourth day, I proposed. On the fifth day, she accepted– hypothetically.

"Let's say I accepted…" she started, as we left my house for a stroll by the river. It was the day before Norooz.

"Hold on, please." I proceeded to the middle of the empty street and did a little happy dance.

Returning by her side, slightly out of breath, I asked, "OK, what were you saying?"

She gave me her beautiful, heart-melting smile and went on with her hypothetical scenario. Something about life in Japan–I don't quite remember.

That night she called me.

"Babak," she said, and I could sense some anxiety in her enchanting voice. "I told my dad."

"Great!"

"You need to come here with your family tomorrow evening at five. Dad wants to see you."

"OK, I'll see if they don't have any plans."

"This is very important."

"OK."

I hung up and went to find Mom and Dad. They were sitting in the living room.

"Mom, we are going to Jila's place tomorrow afternoon," I said, abruptly.

"You know better than to make plans for my New Year's Day, Babak." Mom sounded slightly annoyed. "We have a million things to do. All the family is coming here, then we have to go visit with your dad's side—"

"You don't understand," I said, forcefully. "This is very important for Jila and me."

"But you can't—" she started.

"Sudi," Dad jumped in. "Sudi, he's serious."

Mom suddenly went quiet. "You mean…?" She looked at me, all puzzled.

"No," I said, "I don't know." I really didn't know if this was an actual official, traditional proposal gathering. I had never pictured myself going through that, but I didn't know what the expectation was on Jila's side. "I just need you guys to come to her place with me and meet her dad. That's all. Jila and I will work out the rest."

Mom sat down staring into nowhere. She looked nervous and stunned. "But… I don't know what to do. What do we say? I've never done this before."

"Let me ask her." I ran to the other room to call Jila.

"Don't say anything about marriage or anything," she said. "It's too early for that. All you have to do is show up with your parents so the two families get to know each other."

"OK."

"You can talk about the weather, I don't know, pollution, traffic, anything but marriage."

***

Jila's dad had separated from her mom, but it was an amicable separation, and her dad consulted with her mom on every important decision related to their three daughters, who had chosen to live with him since a year or so after the separation, when Jila had been nine. Jila's mom was at her dad's place when we got there with my parents, Siamak, and Sara. I shook hands nervously with Jila's dad and he showed us into the tidy, little living room.

"Welcome, welcome." He had a calm, warm voice. "Very pleased to meet you all. Please make yourselves at home."

I was quite nervous and worried, not as much about the impression I would leave, but how my family would fare. After the initial introductions and niceties, Jila's dad, a kind-looking, quiet man, asked me about my studies and my upcoming trip. He smiled and nodded, listening to me, but I couldn't quite read his body language. Was he impressed, or was he politely going through the motions for Jila's sake, mad deep down that this had been sprung upon him? Was he a traditional father? Did he approve of Jila and me having met and made friends on our own?

An awkward silence fell on the house. Jila kept going to the kitchen to fetch fruit and tea, and stayed there for long stretches. This made me nervous and cut me off from my only source of confidence.

"What beautiful weather!" exclaimed Mom, breaking the silence.

"Yes," Jila's dad said, "it's very nice, isn't it? Spring is finally upon us."

"Indeed," Mom confirmed.

Silence.

"There's zero pollution," Mom added.

"Yes." Jila's dad was smiling.

"You can see the mountains again," Mom said.

"You can, can you?" Was he enjoying this?

Silence.

"The traffic was so good we made it here from Zafar in fifteen minutes."

Jila's dad nodded.

Great, I thought, *we just went through all the kosher topics. What do we talk about now? Maybe we should leave?*

"Well!" My dad broke the awkward silence, giving me a jump, "Let's cut to the chase. Jila and Babak are both very smart kids. They know what they want. They love each other and we should defer to them on any decision they might make going forward. I'm sure you'd agree."

What the …? This is unrehearsed! He wasn't supposed to talk. We weren't supposed to say things like that. It's too early. What is Jila's dad going to think? He's going to kick us out. This is preposterous. Of course, he won't let his precious little girl socialize with such open-minded, Westernized, decadent people!

I looked around for Jila and couldn't find her. You could hear a pin drop. She was probably listening from the kitchen, holding her breath like I was.

Her dad's face remained unchanged for a few seconds, and then broke out into a smile. Was I sensing a sign of relief on his part?

"Yes, I agree. My Jila is very smart and knows what's best for her," he said. "I'm fine with whatever she decides."

***

Jila called almost as soon as we got back home.

"My dad likes your family. Especially your dad."

"Really?"

"Listen." She seemed to be in a hurry. "I need you to come back."

"Now?"

"Yes. Mom and Dad didn't really get to know you that well," she said, "and my sister is here now too and would really like to meet."

"But—"

"Please. Can you make it? It's really important for my family to get to know you better."

"I'll be right there."

Suddenly, everything became very complicated. I had thought it was all done and happy after our parents' declarations, but apparently not. My head filled up with questions. *What do they want to ask me? Why weren't they there earlier today? Should I change or would that be too much?*

I ran out after giving Mom a terse explanation as to why I needed the car and where I was going. I drove very fast and got there a bit early, but

I couldn't find their house. I must have parked at the wrong entrance. *These apartment blocks all look the same.* I looked for the address for twenty minutes before finding it a good mile away from where I'd parked.

Jila opened the door and invited me in.

"My uncle's family is here too," Jila said, as she led me into a packed living room. Had they all come to meet me or was this a New Year's Day get-together?

Jila's sister offered me the 'comfortable' couch. I sank into it and, looking up, I was confronted by a neat semi-circle of curious eyes, staring down at me. Everyone was very cordial and nice, but I became increasingly self-conscious. My every move was being scrutinized. My every word was being interpreted and reinterpreted in their minds as they tried to answer the ultimate question of the day: was I good, or was I evil?

Someone asked me if I planned to come back after my studies in Japan. I started answering that I had not planned anything, and that the decision would be for Jila and me, should we go together. This is when Jila's sister offered me an orange.

I looked at the fruit with dread. It would be rude not to take the offer. *This is part of the test. They want to see me peel an orange. What if I screw up? What if I cut too deep and make a mess? What if I don't make deep enough cuts and have to peel off the white stuff? How do I hold the knife? Is it the same as when we peel a cucumber or is there a different technique? How wide should each leaf of the peels be? Do I start with the circle on the top? Which side is the top anyway?*

I managed to survive the orange, somehow, and answered the questions. Thank God for Jila's brother-in-law. He asked me about my master's thesis and seemed to be listening to my explanations with interest, and that changed everything. This was my comfort zone and I soon regained full self-confidence.

Dinner was a very tasty dish of chicken-with-rice. We all sat at the table and started eating. They offered me a drink, but Jila had a hard time opening the family-sized soda bottle. She passed it to her sister, who gave up after a few attempts. Jila's dad wasn't able to open it either.

"Can I help?" I offered.

"No, no," the brother-in-law said, "I got it." He tried his luck using the tablecloth for friction.

But the bottle was not cooperating.

"We've got to get some air under the lid," someone said, and they went to the kitchen.

"Heating the lid works too," Someone else suggested, following the bottle.

Before long, everyone but Jila's four-year-old nephew and I had left the table. I could hear concerned whispers from the kitchen, as they tried using some sort of a cutting knife or saw to decapitate the bottle of orange soda. Clearly, I was not the only one concerned about the impression I made that day.

***

The last few days before my departure were like a whirlwind. Jila and I met almost every day and spent countless hours on the phone. We had our first little argument, but most of our time together was spent in a state I can only describe as floating in a thick, soft, happy, pink haze. I kept discovering new lovely beautiful things about her, often after she'd departed and as I lay on my bed, dazzled and dazed, thinking about her.

There was no time to officially get married and sign the papers. Dad and I went to a local notary and I signed some papers giving him full authority while I was away. Mom, who'd already planned a goodbye party for me, sent invitations to Jila's family to join in. I taught Jila some basics of using a personal computer and introduced her to the cutting-edge, new technology called email.

A day before departure, we went to the Japanese Embassy. The officials there politely walked us through the process of applying for a visa for Jila, and gave me the paperwork to notify the Monbusho authorities of this imminent change in my status. I was very uncomfortable with the whole thing and laughed nervously when they reminded me of the fact that I had rejected the Iranian government scholarship because I didn't want to get married. I didn't want them to think I had been deceptive. But there was no easy way to explain what had happened.

On our way out, the embassy assistant called me.

"Mr. Hodjat." She was smiling. "You are leaving in a couple of days, yes?"

"I am," I said, smiling back. "Thanks for everything, Miss, you've been very helpful."

She held out her hand, and I shook it after hesitating a moment. Opposite sexes didn't usually shake hands in public, but I guess we were technically in Japan, and the fact that she wasn't wearing a veil made it more normal.

"I must say," she said, "when you called yesterday and told me about your fiancée, I thought…" She hesitated.

"Yes, I understand."

"But I see you two together now, and I can see that I was mistaken. You make a good couple."

I looked at Jila, waiting for me patiently at the door. Facing the unknown world together with her was a thrilling thought.

"Yes," I said, "thank you. I think we do."

***

On the thirteenth day of the year, Iranians go out of town, picnicking, to avoid the jinx of the number thirteen. On that day, I left home for good.

Leaving home, your parents, your siblings, your grandparents, your friends, your town… it's not easy. On top of all of that, I was leaving Jila. The past three weeks had been an emotional rollercoaster for me, but today, I was fighting hard not to cry. I joked a lot. So did Siamak, and my uncle's wife, Elham, who kept making fun of my passport picture.

Mom was quiet. She joked too. Most of all, she kept giving me advice till the last minute. Years later, I saw the home video of that day, and was shocked to find out that the moment I left and the door was shut, everyone—Siamak, Elham, Mom—everyone had cried.

Dad dropped me off at the airport, hugged me, and simply said goodbye. "OK, Jila," he said, "I'll wait in the car for you."

I held Jila's hands tightly for a few moments staring into her eyes.

"You will come," I said.

"Of course."

"You will come."

She smiled. "I will come," she said softly, and I let go.

***

Japan was amazing. My living environment had changed so much, so suddenly, it seemed like my brain was in constant overdrive to learn everything new. New language, new home, new town, new daily routine, new friends. Good friends. Like friends you make in the military, but this time, in a challenging but fun setting.

As Monbusho students, we had to take a six-month language crash course before starting at our respective departments. I'd bike to the main campus every day and join students from all nationalities, sitting in a class not dissimilar to first grade, learning to speak, read, and write in a very different language—except for the Chinese who didn't have a problem writing Japanese, but seemed to be bottom of the class when it came to reading or comprehension.

After language class, I would head out to my professor's lab once or twice a week. The lab was on a different campus on the outskirts of town. I had my own desk and computer there, with high-speed internet.

I made some friends at the international students' dorm too, where we were housed during our first year. I played soccer and made it into the international students' team and found friends that way as well. Before long, I knew most of the international students and even had a few Japanese friends from the lab.

I saved up a lot, knowing Jila would be joining me sooner or later and that the Monbusho pay would not change. I also started working part-time with an agency that sent me out on English tutoring assignments.

Phoning Iran was out of the question, given the price. I wrote letters to Jila almost every day, and emails, sometimes, but she only replied to them when she visited with my parents, and in short sentences; she wasn't used to a keyboard.

Three months after leaving home, Jila and I decided that it simply wasn't practical for me to return to Iran for our wedding. It would be too expensive, and I wouldn't be able to take more than a week off for the trip anyway. We'd simply have to get the official papers signed by proxy in order to get Jila her visa and have her fly out to join me.

On that fateful summer afternoon, I logged into my email account to find a message from Mom already in my inbox. It was right after lunch, on a Saturday, and I was in the dorm computer room, occupying one of five seats. The computer room was crowded that day, as was usually the case on weekends.

It is D-Day, Babak. We will all be at the marriage notary at noon, read Mom's email.

The unwritten courtesy rule was not to hog a computer for more than an hour, but that day was special for me. I had an old photo of Jila in my wallet and I had placed it in the corner of the monitor to keep me company. I kept reading news sites and soccer blogs, and returning to hit 'refresh' on my inbox for news from home. I did get quite a few updates through the day:

Kaivan is here. He will be your witness.

Babak—Kaivan here. Did you see the Liverpool game? They didn't show it in Iran but I saw the highlights…

Dear Babak, we've arranged a little party at our place for after the signings. Nothing big; it's kind of silly without you. Jila's parents and sister will be here…

Babak-jaan, this is your dad. It is an honor for me to sign on your behalf. It's a little bit like getting married again. I'll be heading out to the notary with Kaivan and Siamak in a few minutes. Mom is staying home as we will have a few guests…

I tried to respond to every email. I didn't like the thought of a wedding party with an absent groom. It was common in Iran, especially for guys who emigrated and had a wife practically sent to them by post. I hated the idea of those arranged marriages and the image of a bride in a full bridal gown standing next to a picture frame disturbed me. I realized the fact that signing the papers made our commitment to each other official, but without me there, I thought of this day as a simple bureaucratic step that had to be taken in order to get the visa.

Babak, Jila is being late. Amir just called from the notary. We're not sure what happened. I'm trying to track them down, but their number is engaged.

Somehow, at this point, the emails stopped. An agonizing hour passed. I kept sending emails, but got nothing.
It's nothing, I thought, *she must have been stuck in traffic or something.*
But deep down I started to worry. Surely, she wouldn't be late for this. I went back and read the last email I had from her from a couple of weeks back, but there was no trace of doubt in it. There was nothing

I could do from here. She had no way of contacting me. Maybe I should go make a phone call? But Mom had said her number was engaged.

I kept pressing the 'refresh' button, frantically hoping for an update.

Mom! For crying out loud, send me something!

I kept sending short messages.

Mom, any updates?

Were you able to reach Jila? Did they make it to the notary?

Should I call? Please respond.

Hello…?

I kept rotating between the inbox, the spam folder, and the deleted items, in case I had deleted something by mistake.

I took Jila's black and white photo I had placed on the monitor and held it in my hand. I didn't believe in praying, but somehow, concentrating on what I really, *really* wanted, while holding her tiny little photo in front of me and staring at it seemed to be the best I could do at that moment. Maybe it was tricking my brain into thinking it actually had a role in directing the events unfolding many thousands of miles away.

"Come on, come on, come on, come on…"

In my mind, I was watching a soccer game online, over a flaky connection, with Jila on the ball about to take a shot, and the image frozen.

Argh!

I was getting ready to leave, when a '1' appeared on the blue mailbox icon.

Congratulations! it read. *You are now officially married to Jila!*

"YIPEE!" I screamed. I couldn't contain myself. I started dancing around my chair and making happy noises. I looked around to see if there was anyone with whom I could share my joy. That's when I noticed the time. It was dark and there was no one left in the computer room except for one of the American undergrads whom I didn't know too well.

He was gazing at me with a face that looked like a question mark.

"I just got married!" I explained, and went back to read the rest of the email and to write a response.

The whole thing must have looked very strange, with me barefoot, in my trainer shorts and t-shirt, sitting at the computer, singing loudly to myself.

After sending the email, I felt the pang of hunger and got up to find something to eat. The undergrad was still in the same position I'd seen him a few minutes ago, staring at me in disbelief.

"Wanna grab dinner?" I asked him. "I'm celebrating at McDonald's. I'll buy you a burger."

"Um, I don't know…"

"Come on!"

"OK," he said, and he shut down his computer and followed me as I boogied out the door.

***

Jila was coming. Finally! My days of preparation and waiting would be over that day.

Six weeks had passed since our official wedding by proxy. I had moved to a couple's apartment in the dorm just a few days before, and any time I could find after school I was spending cleaning up and tidying. I'd sent a letter to Jila a couple of weeks ago with details on what to expect or do every step of the way on her journey to Fukuoka. She'd never been abroad before and her English wasn't that good. I'd asked Haero, the only one of my friends who owned a car, if he'd give me a ride to the airport to pick her up.

As I waited at the gate, bouquet of flowers in hand and Haero by my side, I reviewed all the things I wanted to tell her. All that I had experienced, all that I had discovered, all that I had thought, all my feelings, all the places I wanted to show her, all my friends I wanted her to meet. Everything. Everything.

"Jila!" I waved frantically, and ran to embrace her.

She was so beautiful; more beautiful than I'd remembered her every moment of being away from her. And she was warm. And her smile was enchanting. She'd not been a dream. She was there and she was real.

"There's so much I have to tell you," she said.

Back home, my friends surprised us by throwing Jila a welcome party, cake, decorations, and all. They helped with her luggage, introduced themselves and welcomed her, and left quickly thereafter.

"You've been away from each other for too long," Kerman, my Tunisian friend, explained. "You have a lot of catching up to do. I'll see you later, my friend." He winked.

As soon as I shut the door, a feeling of dread and panic overwhelmed me. We were alone now, just me and her. This was the beginning of our life together. She had braved thousands of miles to be with me, and we hardly knew each other. What if it was all a great, big, tragic mistake?

"Babak," her sweet voice called me from the other room, and all my worries evaporated.

EPILOGUE: THE STORY

*H*ere I go again. It's crunch time and I'm starting yet another project. I need to merge our version 9.51 and 9.25 changes, port the new volume indicator to C, and upgrade our evolutionary training run as soon as possible. At the same time, I have to help come up with a better engagement algorithm than first-come-first-served. The skip-probability approach isn't as promising, and would sound ad-hoc to investors. (Funny how an evolutionary system with an initial random population sounds scientific to these guys while skip-probability sounds ad-hoc. Maybe it's because we've started to call it Skippy.)

But why am I so distracted? I asked that very question from my sixth-grade son, Arash, last night. I'm reading him *The Three Musketeers*, and I've noticed lately that I have to reread each paragraph to him. His mind wanders. Pre-adolescence? Am I stuck in that age too?

I always started new projects at the worst time. I translated *The House at Pooh Corner* into Persian in the heat of the Konkoor, Iran's nationwide university exams. I used to go to bed early and wake up at 3 a.m. every day to study. I'd turn the light on and go back to bed giving myself 'ten more minutes' of waking up time. The light at 3 a.m. is brutally piercing.

It keeps you awake, but barely. I would lie there staring into the light, reorganizing my to-do list as time passed. Once I started the translation project, though, I was up before the alarm clock, working on it. *You can do it if it helps you out of bed*, I decided.

I'd work on the book for an hour or so, switch to my studies for ten minutes, and then pick up one of the five novels I was reading. This was my 'recess' time. I'm a slow reader, but I must have finished thirty books during the pre-Konkoor period.

I passed. Didn't have much of a choice. It was either that or the military service, which wasn't much of an option given the war. I still remember Teri's astonished face, staring at me from the front seat of my uncle's car as we were double-parked, waiting for my dad to get back.

"You would?"

My uncle's American wife had just asked me if I'd pick up a gun and fight for the mullahs, should a war break out. To me the question was very hypothetical. I was twelve! Who'd expect me to fight?

"Of course! I don't see it as fighting for the mullahs. I'd be fighting for my country."

Her words echoed in my ear during the roughest moments I had, both times I was drafted. Like the night I decided to kill time singing in my head all the songs I knew by heart. I was on the 2 a.m. four-hour guard shift, my second draft boot camp—this time the police force—and I was homesick.

It's been something, seeing you again
And in this time we had to spend
It's been good to be around
I thank you for that special thrill
You keep me going on until
The next time I'm in town...

Now why this particular song brought me to tears that night, I don't know. Could be because it reminded me of my best friend, Masoud, and how we sang it together, with him at the keyboard and me struggling with the chords on my guitar. He was in America now, having vowed never to return.

"The only thing I'm saying," I had said to him sternly, a few days before he left, "is that I think you shouldn't burn any bridges behind you. You know, just in case you ever change your mind and want to come back."

For the first time during our long walk, he stopped and turned to look me in the eye.

"Babak, let me tell you a story. As medical student interns at Tehran University, we have a weekly meeting amongst ourselves where we discuss issues between us and make recommendations to the hospital management. In the last meeting I got into a little bit of a debate with one of the hezbollahi interns. This guy is a big-shot in the medical department's Islamic society. He was saying we should recommend tighter screening of student interns based on Islamic values so as to culturally elevate the status of the student body. All I was saying was that we should consider scientific merit instead. The guy looked me in the eye and said the country did not need faithless people like me. As far as he was concerned, our services were not welcome in the academic world of the Islamic Republic.

"Babak, what are we doing here? Why should we bust our butts for people who think they don't even need our help? I've paid my dues. I worked in the poorest villages of Khuzestan for three years. You only live once, Babak, and I know in a few years I'll forget all of this and I'll get all sentimental about my country and I'd want to come back. I'm preempting that. I *want* the bridges all completely burnt and destroyed."

He had chosen medicine to serve people.

I had chosen software because I liked to play games on my uncle's Commodore 64.

Masoud came in 14th in the Konkoor, back in 1985. We got our rankings together, his parents driving us to pick up our scores. His parents patted him on the head gently and congratulated him, but they were very quiet as we drove a few blocks further to where I would get my results. They were almost pale with worry as I got off the car to find the 'H' sign hanging over the fences, from behind which my life's future would be handed to me on a piece of paper. Everyone was in an anxious mood. Strangers were bragging about how low their ranks were.

"I got 250, how did you do?"

"Dude! You must be Einstein's incarnate. I got 325."

I gazed over their shoulders and noticed they were talking in a scale of 1/1000th.

I was feeling a bit dizzy and the numbers were dancing in front of my eyes as I tried to focus on my ranking. Six hundred and eighty-three. Whew! That meant a university in Tehran was not far-fetched, and I had a little bit of a choice. Most importantly, that meant I would not be drafted. Not yet.

"Six hundred and eighty-three," I said, with a big smile when I returned to the car. Masoud's mom burst into tears of relief and hugged me. His dad shook my hand warmly.

Wow! I thought, *these guys were more worried about me than they were for their own son!*

***

I'm reading this again now in Hong Kong. Fixed a bunch of typos. My internet connection is slow and I'm too jet-lagged to work. Our meetings in Singapore went well yesterday. The evolutionary algorithm has produced some good back-test results and we're starting to talk to people to raise the fund. My partner has started to mix some biological analogies into the pitch. I thought he took it too far yesterday, but it seemed to have worked with the hedge fund manager we pitched it to. I noticed a hint of vindication in his tone as we wrapped the meeting up.

"You come from Iran and work in the US where more than sixty percent of the population doesn't believe in evolution," he said, smiling.

"It makes me cringe every time I hear people refer to evolution as a theory," I said. "Evolution is real and very powerful, as you see from these results."

He looked at me, silent and thoughtful, for a few seconds. "Many people don't make that connection, though."

He was right. Proving that intelligence, evolution, and life can be created virtually has been my life's quest, mainly as my way to prove religion wrong. Somewhere in the depths of my mind, I picture myself demonstrating a system that outdoes humans in their most valued accomplishment: intelligence, while having been created from a completely random base. At the end of this imaginary presentation, I look at the audience triumphantly. Their faces are stunned. They aren't saying anything, but I can see that in their minds, the cobwebs of religion are clearing away. A grand, bloodless, final triumph of science.

An answer to people like my eighth-grade religious studies teacher, who'd look you in the eyes, very kindly and father-like, encouraging you to ask if you have doubts. "...for Islam doesn't want you just to accept things on face value. You are free to ask, challenge, experiment."

One time, he finished this very sentence as I slowly raised my hand. "Ask," he gestured at me, "and anyone in their right minds will ultimately see that Islam is the true and righteous way."

"If God is just, why did he create evil?"

He smiled. "A good question." He walked up to me and continued in a soft, understanding voice. "God created evil to test us."

"But why are we being tested?"

"To determine your devotion and submission to your creator, of course."

"But doesn't he already know that? Isn't he the all-knowing?"

"He is, but *you* don't know it. This is for you."

"Is it? Why? That doesn't make sense?" I was truly confused.

He walked up to me slowly, maintaining his kindly smile. "Look, son. There are certain questions we simply don't ask. Islam is the religion of submission. There are certain things you simply have to accept."

Imagine how surprised I was when, that very evening, at home, my uncle walked down the stairs from his smoked-up room, asking my mom, "Does God exist?"

She was surprised, but went with it. "I don't think so."

My uncle would spend days in his room chain smoking and 'working.' I was too young to know what he worked on. He read a lot of books. Later, when he was in prison, I found the complete works of Marx and Lenin neatly packed in boxes in his room. And poetry books. And all sorts of other books on all sorts of political and socialistic subjects. He used to listen to the same tape of Parisa over and over again. The song he liked the most was a revolutionary Bahar poem set to traditional music: *Tulips have grown out of the drops of blood shed by the nation's youth.*

Uncle Siamak gave my mom a smile, like a hunter, happy to find prey in his trap. He then, through a series of follow-up questions, proceeded to prove to my mom that God did indeed exist.

"So, don't you think there should be a creator?" he asked, in conclusion.

"Yes, but…"

"But…?"

"But…" She looked at my uncle helplessly.

Uncle Siamak smiled again. His trap was working well. He then proceeded with another barrage of questions, this time proving that God did not exist.

"So, can there be a creator?"

"Well, I guess not."

My uncle laughed out loud. He got up, picked the mug of coffee my grandma had poured him, and headed up to his room again, leaving confusion and admiration in his wake.

Mom has retold this story to us many times. She says it with pride. Sometimes I think she intentionally played into my uncle's hand that day. I think she saw what was coming. She may even have thought of that conversation as a good story to retell just as it was unfolding. That's my mom for you. As a family, we never tired of listening to her retell a story for the tenth time. To us, what had happened was interwoven with all other less significant events that happen in a day. Her distilling it into a story to retell made it gain a certain significance. It made me proud just to have been there.

I was there, too, in her other story about the mosquito net. Uncle Siamak would leave for a few days at a time. It was after the war had started and we had taken refuge at my grandparents', and this provided for the brief period in which I lived with him and got to know him a bit.

On one occasion when my uncle had not returned for a couple of days, my grandfather unlocked his door and let in a worker to install mosquito netting on his window. I remember my uncle coming back the next day and heading to his room. A short while later he lit a cigarette and opened his window. He started cursing loudly and banging and tearing at the mosquito net. He then burst out of his room and tossed the shredded net at our feet.

"Don't ever do this again," he said in a low, angry voice that made me shudder. "I hate it!"

It must have taken me a lot of nerve, a few months later, to insert tiny exploding sticks into his cigarettes and listen to him light three up in succession, then throw the pack out and walk out to buy a new one. When he came back home with a new pack in his hand, he noticed Sia and I hiding our laughter in the hallway and asked whether we had anything to do with this. I nodded and he laughed out loud. "I thought the cigarettes were bad!"

I remembered that laughter six months or so later as my mom and grandma were standing in the stairway laughing. It was a strange kind of laughter, this one: out of place, somewhat forced, out of context.

My mom had just gotten home with news that my uncle was at Evin.

"All three of them are there now," she said with a big smile, and my grandma burst into laughter...

I guess women don't laugh at funny things. They laugh for other reasons. It's much more of a communication tool.

I laugh when it's funny. Just as I cry when I'm sad.

I don't, really. I'm lying. I seldom cry. When I do, it's usually because I really, really miss someone. And sometimes, not even then. This used to worry me a lot. Like when I got home from school one day to find my grandma, Maman Bahram, and her sisters sitting on the rug with puffed faces, looking utterly miserable.

"Did your ships sink or something?" I asked, immediately regretting it.

"They killed your uncle."

I didn't even break my stride. I turned into my room, placed the headphones on my ears, and proceeded to play the electric organ for the next two hours. I felt embarrassed for what I'd said, as well as what I had not said. I felt afraid to confront them again and was wondering how long I should stay there before they left and it was safe to come out of my room. And I felt relieved that I had the organ to drown out all the outside sounds.

I did not feel sad. I did not cry. I had always wondered how I'd react if someone close to me died. What would I do if Mom had a heart attack, or if Dad was hit by a car? I was worried I would not be sad enough. I worried that my philosophy of life would make me heartless. When distant relatives died, I found all the wailing and exaggerated grief funny. Aren't we guaranteed to die someday? Why are people so stunned when it actually happens? Death is what makes evolution work.

***

"We create the first population by creating randomly generated rule-sets for each individual."

"Random?"

"Yes. We have a palette of conditions and actions we choose from by chance and put together to form the behavior of each individual in the population. We then evaluate each individual, and rank order the population from best to worst. Now all of these guys are going to be pretty bad, but some will be 'less bad' than the others."

The investor listens attentively.

"Then we keep the top five percent and kill off the rest."

"I love it!" She's ecstatic and I'm taken aback. To me, the most interesting part of what we do is the fact that we essentially use random functions to get the computer to generate useful code.

To her, the keyword seemed to be death. Since that first meeting, every time I hear her pitch our company to someone, she pauses right after the description, looking for some affirmation of her excitement.

"Isn't it great? And if they don't perform, we kill them!"

I did finally cry over someone's death, in my mid-thirties, after being on the phone to Iran for what seemed like an eternity, listening to my uncle, and then my dad, explaining the detail of what happened and why.

"So, by the second stroke your grandpa was unconscious and died in peace. Blood flow to his brain was disrupted, so he must have been in a vegetative state for the last few hours. He seemed to be sleeping, and at times his eyes were open, but he didn't respond to anything. His heartbeat and blood pressure were OK. The pacemaker must have been working well. He was in his nineties and had a good life…"

I really didn't care. I wasn't sad because I feared death. Death, in my mind, was still a necessary inevitability. The end of a person was still not sad to me. It was the end of my grandpa, Baba Javad, that was heart-wrenching. The end of a one-of-a-kind, soulful, cheerful, funny, smart, charming, kind, bald, beautiful human being, whose smile was vibrant, and whose presence was fun. Who taught me to play backgammon, and who said silly, meaningless things, just because he felt like it. Who was devastated by the loss of his second child, but seldom showed it. Who lived, for sixty-five years, with a wife who had no sense of humor, but loved him, reluctantly. For who could resist such a character?

***

I ran into Chris in a cafeteria at Kyushu University in 1997. He was cool and charming and won me over immediately. I must have been in my wisecracking mood with my little audience of international students, laughing along, when he started complementing my performance with his own cracks. After lunch, he came up to me and introduced himself as a med school grad student. I liked him.

I liked him, I think, for the same reason most people liked Chris on their first encounter: he had a talent for mirroring and reflecting the best of your own self back at you. I guess liking him made you like yourself more, in some way. It was only later, when you witnessed him with other folks, that you wised up to his technique. After a while, you wondered, *Who is this guy anyway? Do I even know him?*

Chris asked me about my work, and as usual, I hesitated at first. You know, I think of myself as very pragmatic, and want people to think of me that way, but somehow, I'm always working on some out-of-this-world ambitious project, and I feel, if I'm not careful at how I explain what I'm up to, that I'll come across as unrealistic. Wishy-washy, as was my childhood nickname.

"I came up with a multi-agent system that's really powerful. You know, a kind of distributed AI. I feel like I've proven to myself that AI is possible, and that Alife is possible, and as a finale to my career, I want to prove this to the world through some cool application."

"Wow! That's ambitious. I've read about AI a bit and I know some programming. Can you tell me more about your system?"

"Well, it's a multi-agent system." Back then calling something agent-based was hip. It was the new AI. But everyone had their own definition for an agent, ranging from a tiny specialized piece of code that simply solved part of a problem distributed over many agents, to a great, big multi-faceted piece of code that was meant to be a human's representative, say, in crawling the web. "It can be used to solve complex problems. At least to approximate a solution."

"Cool! How did you come up with it?"

Seeing his genuine enthusiasm, I decided to give him the story that I gave the folks in the Japanese Consulate when they interviewed me for the Monbusho scholarship. *My* theme, which seemed, so elegantly, to string together my random career decisions.

Basically that, at fifteen, I had gotten interested in computers because I loved the challenge of beating computer games on my uncles' Commodore 64. I had browsed through the leaflet with the list of university majors for a math grad and had found them all uninteresting, except for 'computer engineering,' which had conjured up memories of the sixth floor of the Science Museum in London when I was eleven, trying to outsmart a giant computer in what I found out later to be a game based on a simple binary search algorithm.

The truth is, there were interesting subjects under the biology grad list. Some pretty good ones under literature, and even some good ones under arts. I was a math grad, though. And that meant 'computer software engineering.' All else looked boring.

I wish I could say I was a math grad because I loved math or hated everything but math. The reality is that on that fateful day in the summer of '82, as I walked down to the high school with my dad, I didn't care one way or other. Halfway there, Dad finally broke the silence. "So, what will it be?"

"What?"

"What subject are you picking for high school?" We had to pick one before the start of tenth grade.

"Oh. Um… biology," I decided, then and there.

"Really? How fabulous! That is just fantastic! You're going to study in my field. Of course, you can become a doctor if you want. I started off wanting to be a doctor, but ended up an entomologist. I mean you aren't limited to med school. Take your time and see what you like before you decide." He was ecstatic. After another block or two: "That is just great! I will help you. In fact, you can get help from all my friends."

Dad was a professor of entomology and taught at the university down in Ahwaz, nine hundred kilometers away. He was what they called a 'flying professor.' He lived in Tehran and flew down to Ahwaz, which was closer to the war zone, teaching two weeks a month.

"I can't believe my son is following in his father's footsteps. Of course, you don't have to become a university professor. You don't have to go to med school either…"

He was having a lot of fun with this, all the way to the school. When we finally got to the office, the school vice-principal fished out my file and looked for my name on it.

"So, Mr.… Hodjat…" He looked at me from above his glasses. "What is your decision, sir?"

"Biology."

"Biology?" He was looking at my scores from last year.

"Yes."

"Are you sure? You got an A in geometry last year. Only a handful of kids got anything above C. And let's see…" He flipped a few pages. "Your math scores are outstanding. Are you sure you've given it enough thought?"

"Well…"

"Your biology score is good too, but there are only a few students that have enrolled in math this year, and your math is good. There will be at least three biology classes to a single math class, which means you'll get an excellent teacher-to-student ratio. Maybe you should take some time and think—"

"OK then, math."

"Pardon me?"

"Sign me up for math."

"Are you sure?"

"Sure."

My dad was very quiet on the way home. I was thinking about weekend plans with Masoud, so I didn't even notice that he was there until he finally commented, half to himself, "I can't believe you made such a huge life decision just like that." He threw up his shoulders and it was the end of it.

My dad's OK.

***

Chris called me over at lunch the next day.

"Can you talk?"

"What's up?"

"I thought about your agent AI system. I've got a great idea for a company," he whispered.

I was surprised. *I hardly know this guy and he wants to start a company based on a terse description I gave him of my research?*

"So, I was at a bar last night with my buddy, Yokoishi, the CEO of Atmark," he explained. "We noticed the mama-san at the bar was trying to get the baseball game on TV, but she just couldn't find the channel or work the remote. She finally gave up on it and called her son."

He stopped and looked at me with a big smile expecting me to start sharing his excitement, but I simply couldn't link Chris's story to anything I'd said about the technology.

"She said, 'Get me the baseball game!' and her son took the remote away from her and found the channel and changed to it."

My look must have been puzzled.

"Don't you get it? The son was the agent!"

Oh! I did get it. Chris had totally misunderstood my description of the technology. I had mentioned the distributed AI as 'a society of agents,' and all he'd heard was the word 'agent.'

I laughed, but before I could explain his misunderstanding, he started describing his vision.

With words pouring out of him in rapid fire, and sometimes hitting me in the face in the form of spit, he described a system that would use my 'AI' to help people get to the programming they wanted on their TV sets. He talked about how Yokoishi-san had accepted to fund a start-up around this idea, with me as the CTO, and how we'd go to California and make it happen.

How naïve can you get? I thought. *This is beyond naïve. This guy is crazy.*

"Look, Chris," I interrupted him. "Listen to me. To build a system like what you describe you'd need Speech Recognition software, which is really hard to build, and the state of the art is totally inadequate. Plus, the real AI is going to be in the language understanding. Natural Language processing is very difficult. I worked on it before. It's a tough problem."

I explained to him all the reasons why the system he was describing was next to impossible to build. He listened patiently, but his eyes were staring into a far-off place.

He smiled. "Babak, it may be difficult, but it's doable. You said you believed in the power of AI and were looking for a way to prove it to the world. Well, here's your opportunity. Here's a difficult problem no one else can tackle. Think about it."

"Yes, but—"

"Just think about it." He patted me on the back. "Let's meet tomorrow and tell me what you think."

***

I did think about it. The challenge was appealing. Chris was right. He had the right application in mind, although he knew very little about the technology needed to make it work. A new way to interact with technology: a new user interface–the most important thing since GUIs. It was super ambitious, and I liked it.

Two months later, December, Chris and I set out on an exploratory trip to California to gauge the feasibility of the project. I had two questions I needed to answer before I could commit. Was my approach to solving the project new, and could we fund it?

I had come up with a new multi-agent concept that I was pretty sure would work. I had proved it mathematically and had a paper in the works. Most importantly, my professor had given it his blessing. I made a list of people I wanted to meet while we were in the Valley and they all seemed to be receptive to the concept and, most importantly for me, thought it was novel. The approach seemed so obvious to me that I kept thinking someone else must have invented it before.

Chris had gotten an intro to a famous Japanese permanent resident businessman by the name of Menjo-san, who was a principal at a start-up consulting firm. It was the height of the dot-com craze, and Menjo-san seemed to be coaching us in ways to plan the business and grow it, but I thought all of that was secondary.

"How are we going to get the money to build it?" I asked him, finally.

He looked at me with a smile and said, "Oh, this is easily fundable. If you give me the right pitch and show me a demo, I can pick up the phone right now and get you a hundred thousand dollars tomorrow."

That had done it for me. Straight away, out of the meeting, we went to the local Fry's electronics superstore. I bought Dragon Naturally Speaking speech recognition software, a Hauppaugge TV tuner kit that plugged into your desktop, and Borland's Java development environment software (I wanted to learn a new programming language too). I started coding that night, and had the first demo done in a few weeks.

***

I like the guy. He's smart. We seem to share some experiences. I mean, beyond the fact that we both started using personal computers around the same time. Of course, we did geek out on that, bragging about writing Z80 assembler language within sixty-four kilobytes, or using a five-megabyte Winchester hard drive. But he was also a fellow entrepreneur. He too had started a few companies before. He too had experienced the rollercoaster ride of successes, failures, rebounds, and exits. He had the sparkle in his eyes and the marks of experience in his frown.

"Yeah, it's all about timing," he says. "You can build the best thing since sliced bread, but if your timing is off, it'll amount to nothing."

I laugh. "You know, after a full year of hard work on a prototype in my first start-up…" I pause for effect, knowing he's probably wondering how this is relevant to timing. "We had a tiny office on the second floor of an Indian restaurant, downtown Mountain View."

"Oh! When was this?" he asks, enthusiastically, already looking for a related story in his head.

"Nineteen ninety-eight."

"Cool!" he says, with fake enthusiasm. Obviously, the date has not helped him with his background quest.

"So, our technology allowed you to control a bunch of devices using natural language." I don't think he knows what that means. "You know, talking to an app like you're talking to a friend."

He nods.

"I had a TV set, a satellite receiver with five hundred channels, a DVD." I smiled. "You remember those, right?"

He chuckles.

"We even had a light switch attached to it."

"Turn the lights off?" he asks, clapping his hands.

"Exactly! So, I really wanted to get this right, not the least because this guy was the chairman of Borland. But I made a fatal mistake…" Pause for effect. "I told him he can command the devices and say whatever he wants, and handed him the headset microphone."

"Dragon?" he guesses correctly.

"Yes."

"So, what happened?"

"Well, he put the headset on, hesitantly, and just sat there."

"Didn't say anything?"

"Nothing!"

"How come?"

"He just sat there, for a long time, thinking intently," I say. "I was completely confused." Another pause. "He finally turns to me with a grin and says, 'This is very difficult for me. You see, I've never talked to my TV set before.'"

We both burst out laughing.

"So, you see," I conclude, "you can make the TV so smart it can understand your commands, whatever way you say them, but if the timing is wrong, nobody would want to!"

"That's right. Obviously, no Siri back then."

And this is where I made the mistake.

"You know, Siri was inspired and has borrowed hard from what we built at my first start-up, Dejima."

"Really?"

"Yes!" I say, and feel like I have to prove it, and go on to summarize the links. Halfway through, I start regretting it. I am making him uncomfortable, and the meeting is really about my completely unrelated latest start-up.

He is fidgeting, and I can tell that he doesn't have anything to use to one-up me.

But he manages to come up with one.

"You know, I invented the laptop," he says finally.

"Really?"

"I did." He nods. "But I was naïve enough to give it away."

"Oh," I say. "You mean you signed the patent away?"

"No! No! No patents. I just showed my design to some folks."

Disbelief must be written all over my face.

"I was working for IBM at the time…" and he goes on to explain the whole thing in more detail.

I joked about his claim to my partner later on.

"You know, this guy was claiming that he invented the laptop!"

"What?"

"I know, right?"

He laughed, but I added, "He wanted to one-up my claim that I'm the inventor of Siri."

A sad thought came to my mind. What if he had the very same reaction of disbelief to my claim as I had to his? It was an uncomfortable feeling I didn't like.

"I'll never make that claim in an intro again," I declared. "It's irrelevant."

I thought about it.

"It's not believable, either."

My partner nodded.

***

I get back to my desk. I need to debug the class-server and look into the synchronization issue when adding genes to the server pool. I can focus now. I'm done writing my story, and it all makes sense. I've articulated a coherent thread, tying everything together, giving it a higher meaning. I can focus now. I've found the story that patches up all my stories, and that's what it's all about, isn't it? Stories.

It's all about the stories.

ABOUT THE AUTHOR

Babak Hodjat is an Iranian-American inventor and tech entrepreneur with a passion for storytelling, soccer, and Artificial Intelligence. Born in England, Babak went to kindergarten in Idaho, attended middle school in London, completed high school and undergraduate studies in Iran, and obtained his PhD in Japan. He has been living and working in California since the late nineties.